Economics for
Construction and Property

D0453224

Economics for Construction and Property

L. Ruddock

B.A., M.Sc.(Econ.), M.Sc., M.I.S.
Senior Lecturer in Construction Economics
Manchester College of Arts and Technology

Edward Arnold
A member of the Hodder Headline Group
LONDON SYDNEY AUCKLAND

Edward Arnold is a division of Hodder Headline PLC
338 Euston Road, London NW1 3BH

First published in the United Kingdom 1992

8 7 6 5 4 3 2
99 98 97 96 95

British Library Cataloguing in Publication Data
Ruddock, Leslie
Economics for Construction and property
I. Title
338.4

ISBN 0 340 56359 1

Typeset in 10/11 Palatino by Wearset, Boldon, Tyne and Wear
Printed and bound in the United Kingdom by
J W Arrowsmith Ltd, Bristol

Contents

To Lewis and Steven

Preface

The purpose of writing this book was to provide a textbook suitable for those students of building, surveying, valuations and property management, who are required to study the subject of economics.

The nature of general economics texts does not always tend to appeal to these vocationally oriented students. For instance, the examples used to illustrate the economic principles are not always seen as relevant. The aim is to provide a textbook which combines an outline of economic principles with illustrations applied to the construction and property industries.

Economics is such a vast field that it is necessary to be selective in the choice of subject matter. The contents of this book were chosen to meet the needs of students taking BTEC courses in construction and property management and the examinations of the Incorporated Society of Valuers and Auctioneers (ISVA). Students taking an economics course for degrees in building, surveying or property management should also find the contents particularly suitable. The sequence of chapters follows a logical progression, yet different students can read the material in the manner which best suits the needs of a particular syllabus.

An important feature of the book is the inclusion of a large number of exercises. The exercises appear at the end of each chapter and give a cross-section of questions from ISVA, BTEC and degree examination papers. Suggested answers to many of these exercises are provided at the end of the book.

Acknowledgements

I am grateful to Times Books for permission to reproduce part of the Top 1000 companies table and to Her Majesty's Stationery Office.

I also thank the Incorporated Society of Valuers and Auctioneers, for permission to reproduce past examinations questions. In any case where I have given a suggested solution, the responsibility is entirely my own.

I should like to thank my wife Pauline for producing the final typescript and also for her patience and support.

Finally, I should like to thank John Clancy for his assistance in designing the cover of the book.

Part One

The Subject Matter of Economics

1

The Economising Problem

It is fair to say that the subject matter of economics is of interest to everyone, because fundamentally economics is concerned with how people satisfy their material (and some non-material) wants. As people's wants are virtually unlimited, but available resources are in limited supply, so it means that people are forced to economise. They must make the most of what they have and use these scarce resources to the greatest advantage.

Economic problems arise as the individual or the community has to make the most efficient use of its limited resources and is confronted with the problem of choice. Economics is accordingly concerned with the arrangements that are made for the use of scarce resources.

1.1 Economic resources

As the production of goods and services to satisfy man's wants is fundamental to a study of economics, it provides a necessary starting point. The production of goods and services calls for the use of what are termed the 'factors of production'. It may appear to be an oversimplification to try to categorise these factors, but three things are basically essential to production.

Land: Includes all those resources provided by nature. This may mean the actual surface of the earth, mineral deposits in the earth or natural crops.

Labour: Consists of the human effort and skill (both mental and physical) involved in production.

Capital: Refers to tools, machinery and equipment of all kinds. In fact anything man-made which is used in production. Accumulating these capital goods is often called *capital investment*.

A fourth factor is sometimes added to the list and may perhaps even be considered to be the most important factor of all. This is termed *enterprise*. There must be a means of organisation to bring together all the things required and to conduct the production process. Simply speaking, enterprise consists of bringing together the other factors at the right time and place.

In all types of production, from peasant farming up to modern industrial mass production, all these elements are required, but obviously in varying proportions. For the peasant farmer harvesting his crop, the land and labour elements are obvious but the capital he uses may consist merely of a simple cutting implement and of course the fourth element consists of his decisions on how and when to carry out his work. Broadly speaking, the more advanced and complicated the production process the more important capital becomes, relative to the other factors. This is certainly true in factory production methods, but even in the building industry, with the advent of systems building and the use of more sophisticated construction plant and equipment, the comparative application of capital has grown.

1.2 Opportunity cost

Economics is concerned only with man's behaviour in relation to scarce means. Those resources whose availability is limited are referred to as economic goods and need to be distinguished from those whose supplies are so plentiful that everyone is able to have as much as he wants. The latter types of good are free goods and have no cost associated with their use.

Under certain circumstances various resources may fall into this category – the supply of water may be such a case in point and the air that we breathe is the foremost example of a non-economic good.

An economic good is therefore a good which has a cost associated with its use. Whenever a choice has to be made between different uses for a resource, the cost with which an economist is concerned is the sacrifice that has to be made by not putting the resource to the use foresaken. The expression opportunity cost is used to indicate the cost of something in terms of the best alternative forgone, and in any situation in which a unit of a resource is being fully utilised the production of one good must necessarily mean that another good cannot be produced.

When a piece of land is being developed for housing then a new factory cannot be built on that site. A person who uses all his available finances to make a deposit on a house he wishes to purchase is unable to also afford to buy a new car. Leisure time is sacrificed by a student who spends his evenings working for his examinations. Whatever the resource (land, money or even time) in these examples, the true economic cost associated with any of these actions is that associated with the alternative forgone. As we shall see, the methods of estimating this cost play a vital role in a study of economics.

1.3 Transformation curves

It may sometimes be the case that perhaps one good has to be rejected in favour of another, but often a decision is made to have a little more of one good at the expense of a little less of the other, i.e. a change at the 'margin'. The following example illustrates such a situation.

A small specialist joinery firm can set its six employees to work producing either doors or window frames and Table 1.1 shows the number of units of

Table 1.1 Production alternatives: doors and window frames

Alternative	Number of workers producing: Doors	Window Frames	Total output of: Doors	Window Frames
A	0	6	0	100
B	1	5	40	94
C	2	4	100	80
D	3	3	132	60
E	4	2	146	40
F	5	1	156	20
G	6	0	160	0

each type of product made when varying numbers of workers are set to work producing them.

The figures in Table 1.1 can be used to draw up a transformation curve (Fig. 1.1) which shows the terms on which the producer can exchange the production of doors for the production of window frames. The curve joins together the combinations of outputs from Table 1.1 and if it is assumed that a worker may spend some time producing one product with the rest of the time spent on the other, then all the possible intermediate points on the curve may be attainable.

The marginal rate of transformation between the two outputs can be calculated from the data. This expresses the cost of one output in terms of the other at the margin, i.e. when an extra (or marginal) worker is switched from one type of production to the other. For instance, the cost of producing the first forty doors is the six window frames (i.e. the difference between ninety four and one hundred) that are no longer produced. Similarly, the cost of producing the first twenty window frames can be expressed as the four doors that would have been produced if six instead of five workers had been producing doors. The marginal rates of transformation when an extra worker is moved from window frame to door production are presented in Table 1.2

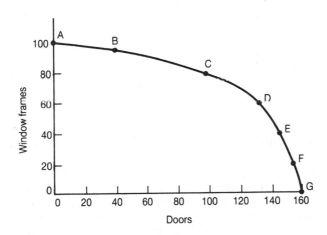

Fig. 1.1 Transformation curve

Table 1.2 Marginal rate of transformation: doors for window frames

Marginal worker	Marginal rate of transformation (Doors gained in terms of window frames)	
	Doors gained	Window frames lost
1	40	6
2	60	14
3	32	20
4	14	20
5	10	20
6	4	20

1.4 Production possibility curves

One of the main purposes of the study of economics is to discover whether the resources of a community are being used efficiently.

The use of a simple example and a diagram called a production possibility curve, which is very similar to a transformation curve, can be used to consider this type of question. To keep matters simple, even though obviously unrealistic, assume that the economy under consideration produces only two goods – wheat and houses. If we also suppose that there is only a fixed amount of resources available and that the state of technology in the economy is stable, then under these circumstances it is possible to work out the various amounts of each of the two goods that the economy is able to produce.

Table 1.3 shows some of the possible alternative combinations of wheat and houses that can be produced.

Table 1.3 Alternative output combinations of wheat and houses

Alternative	Wheat (000 tonnes)	Houses (000 housing units)
A	0	30
B	40	28
C	80	24
D	120	20
E	160	15
F	200	8
G	240	0

For instance, if all the community's resources are used in the production of houses 30 000 houses can be produced, whereas at the other extreme, total commitment to producing wheat would result in an output of 240 000 tonnes. The other alternatives (B to F) are just some of the possible combinations involving the production of both commodities. If we assume that very small adjustments can be made in the allocation of resources between the two types of production, then a production possibility curve can be drawn joining up these points and any point on the curve would represent a feasible combination of the two commodities. This production possibility curve is illustrated by Fig. 1.2. The output of wheat being plotted on the horizontal axis and the output of houses on the vertical.

The more of one good that is produced the less of the other can be produced. The production of more wheat must necessitate the shifting of resources away from house production and vice versa. If for instance, the product mixture was initially at point D on the curve then an increase in the production of wheat by 40 000 tonnes would require that enough resources were moved away from house production so as to necessitate a fall in output of 5000 houses, i.e. a new output combination at point E. The cost of the extra wheat can therefore be measured in terms of the potential housing output forgone.

The downward slope of the curve indicates an opportunity cost of producing more of one type of good in terms of the other good and indeed is more likely to entail a larger and larger opportunity cost, e.g. the opportunity cost of producing the first 40 000 tonnes of wheat when the output combination moves from point A to B is 2000 houses, whereas the production of the next 40 000 tonnes when moving from B to C incurs a loss of 4000 houses. The

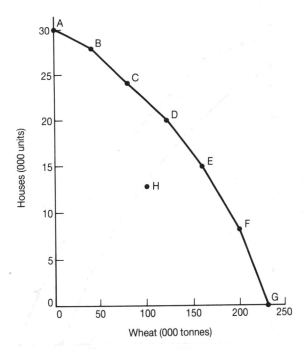

Fig. 1.2 Production possibility curve

reasons for this increasing opportunity cost will be explained when production is considered in more detail.

The combination of all the goods which the community is actually producing can indicate whether or not the community is using its resources efficiently. A combination of goods such as that indicated by point H which is underneath the curve in Fig. 1.2 would mean that the resources of the community were not being fully utilised, i.e. there could be more houses and/or wheat produced using otherwise idle resources. The function of the economic system in operation should be to ensure that this waste does not occur and also to determine the point along the production possibility curve at which the community should operate. A further aim should be to push the production possibility curve outward so that the community has a greater amount of goods to share. Improvements in technology, for instance, could enable more wheat and more houses to be produced from the same amount of resources, as shown in Fig. 1.3. In general, another way would be for a community to devote more of its resources to producing capital rather than consumer goods because capital goods are themselves resources (adding to the other factors of production) and a society doing this will push out its production possibility curve further as growth in the economy occurs.

1.5 Summary

The economic problem must be recognised as one of scarcity. Economists are concerned with considering the costs of allocating scarce resources between different uses and the opportunity cost associated with an alternative forgone

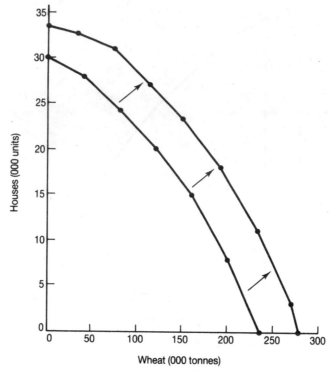

Fig. 1.3 Production possibility curve and economic growth

is their main concern. Transformation and production possibility curves can be used to show alternative allocations of resources.

Exercises

1.1 Indicate, with an explanation, whether the following statements are true or false.
 a) An 'economic problem' cannot be said to exist in a relatively rich country such as the U.K.
 b) If all resources are fully employed, more of one good must result in giving up something of another.
 c) The use of any resource has an opportunity cost associated with it.
1.2 On a particular site a developer is considering a residential development of houses or bungalows (or a mixture of the two). Show how the idea of transformation curves can be used to represent the choices open to him.
1.3 Assume a society's production possibility curve is based on the following combinations:

| | Output | |
Alternative	Food (millions of tonnes)	Houses (millions)
I	0	8
II	6	7
III	10	6
IV	15	4
V	20	0

a) If there are 10 million tonnes of food being produced and 5 million houses, is the society on its production possibility curve? If not what factors could cause this?

b) If the state of technology changes such that twice as many houses as before can be produced at the same levels of food production, plot the new production possibility curve. Can the society now produce 10 million tonnes of food and 10 million houses? If so, is this an efficient combination of outputs?

1.4 With the help of examples, show how the concept of opportunity cost is fundamental to economic analysis.

2

Economic Systems

The essence of economics and the problems involved in the allocation of resources can best be understood by consideration of the questions with which any economic system is concerned. Basically, there are three questions which must be answered. These are; *firstly*, what is to be produced? The community has to decide what collection of goods and services can best satisfy the wants of its citizens. Given its production possibility constraints, it can rule out those combinations of goods which entail economic inefficiency and also the output mixes that are impossible to achieve, but a choice from the feasible combinations still has to be made.

This also involves, of course, the linked issue of how much of each good to produce. Houses may be near the top of society's list of priorities, but how many houses should be produced? How much food? How many cars, roads, power stations, libraries, T.V. sets and so on? The fact that resources are scarce forces society to make these choices. The question also raises the issue of the degree to which a society should be concerned with meeting the needs of its present citizens as against those of its future members. The production of capital goods to provide investment for the future means that less resources can be devoted to produce goods for current consumption. Invariably a balance must be achieved.

Secondly, how are the goods to be produced? Society has to decide how to organise production and to choose the type of firms to produce its goods. The resources available need to be combined in the most efficient way and also there may be choices of technology involved in production.

Thirdly, who should receive the goods and services produced? Again this question involves an element of quantity. Attempts may be made to distribute output on the basis of need. Equal shares for all may be an aim of the system or various degrees of inequality may be deemed desirable. This question, perhaps even more than the others, involves political and moral considerations as well as economic.

2.1 Types of economic system

Basically there are two different means by which these questions can be answered. Under one system individuals are left to their own devices with respect to decisions on what to do with their own privately owned resources. In this free enterprise system the answers to the previous questions are determined by the price mechanism.

The second type of system involves government ownership of the economy's resources in a centrally planned economy. At the extreme, the government may play a totally dominant role in organising economic activity. Land and capital resources may be allocated and workers directed to whatever task the government believes to be most purposeful in the achievement of its objectives. Consumers may find their choice of goods reduced to government determined supplies. On the other hand, the government's role may be quite restricted and consist of mere modifications to the operation of the price mechanism.

2.1.1 The price mechanism

It is useful though to consider initially how the price mechanism operates disregarding any form of government intervention. The simplest way to regard the system is to say that it functions due to two forces. One is 'consumer sovereignty' and the other is the 'profit motive'.

Economists use the term consumer sovereignty to explain how the demands of consumers determine what is produced in the economy. Consumers show relative preferences for various goods and services by the amounts of money which they are willing to spend on them. The more a person wants a good, the more he is willing to spend on that good, and the higher the price he is prepared to pay. In this way, the price system determines which are the most important goods to produce.

The producers of the goods which prove to be the most popular find that the prices tend to be 'bid up', and the effect is that these producers who have made the correct decisions are able to make a profit and will acquire more resources in order to produce even more of the profitable goods. In this way, the profit motive ensures that consumers are supplied with the goods which they require. The system ensures that resources are put only to efficient uses, in the sense that producers not alert to consumer requirements find that the losses they are making on the production of their unpopular goods either forces them out of business or persuades them to move into more profitable lines of production. This means that resources are also attracted to areas where they are productive enough for producers to pay them higher rewards.

The attractions of this apparently simple system of ensuring that consumers' wants are satisfied are obvious. People are able to vote for the goods that they want by exercising their spending power and the market ensures, via the signals of changing prices, that producers respond to the fluctuating patterns of consumers' tastes.

To evaluate the market mechanism though, it is necessary to look at both the benefits and the disadvantages of the system.

2.2 Advantages of the price system

A freely operating price system has certain obvious advantages as a means of resource allocation and the more important of these deserve a mention.

1. Producers are given the necessary incentive (via the profit motive) to produce the goods that consumers want. This also brings about the use of the most efficient production methods.
2. The system involves economic freedom. Production and consumption are

co-ordinated without any coercion. No consumer is forced to purchase from a certain producer; no worker is directed to specific lines of work and people are free to choose their own occupations.
3.   Resources and goods which are scarce sell at high prices and so are carefully used. The high price of petrol for instance, resulting from a shortage, would force motorists to ensure that only essential car journeys are made.

2.3 Problems of the price system

This apparently 'perfect' method of allocating resources does however have several limitations which means that, left to its own devices, it is unable to solve all a society's economic problems.

One major shortcoming concerns the distribution of income in the economy. Whilst the price system may be economically efficient it may still produce a very unequal distribution of income in society. On grounds of fairness and equity, the fact that some individuals are able to reap high rewards from the system whilst others may receive barely sufficient to exist, can be put forward as a major criticism. Intervention by the government to redistribute income is therefore required.

Another problem is that some goods and services simply cannot be provided properly through the price system. Such goods cannot be purchased by individuals in small amounts but can only be consumed on a collective basis. A good example is national defence, which is best left to the government to provide on everyone's behalf. There are a wide number of such social or public goods, which cannot be consumed in individual amounts economically. The price system cannot cater for such social wants.

The market system may also be criticised if there is not a high degree of competition amongst producers and some powerful firms are able to manipulate the market price. At the other extreme though, it may be aruged that resources are wasted if suppliers have to compete with each other by spending vast amounts of money on advertising goods or services which are practically identical to each other – a criticism often levelled at building societies in this country.

Finally, perhaps the biggest problem associated with a freely operating price system is its failure to provide stability in the economy. The existence of periods of high levels of unemployment due to the inability of the price system to necessarily ensure that resources are fully utilised, represents probably the greatest indictment of the system.

On the basis of these disadvantages which are inherent with the market system, it is obvious that a case can be put for some degree of governmental intervention in the operation of the economy. All western countries have 'mixed' economies in the sense that the government shares with the market the role of allocating resources.

2.3.1 The mixed economy

The ways in which the government interferes with the operation of the price system are varied, but overall the role of the government in this area is concerned with eradicating the previously mentioned weaknesses associated with the market system.

In carrying out this task, the functions of the government may be listed as follows:

1. The provision of a suitable environment in which the price system can operate. One service provided by the government is the establishment of a monetary system enabling the exchange of goods and services to be performed efficiently. A legal systen defining the status of consumers and producers is essential to the operation of the market. In the field of property for instance, the legal status of property owners must be well defined with the rights of property buyers and a system for the enforcement of contracts being established. In the construction industry, the provision of a system of building regulations controls the quality of the industry's products for the consumer.

2. Ensuring competition. Competition is the mechanism by which the price system functions properly. The price in a market is determined by the supply and demand decisions of many individual producers and consumers. Producers react to the wishes of consumers and must do so in an efficient manner or suffer the consequences of losses or bankruptcy.

The government may need to protect this system if the number of sellers becomes so small that each seller is able to exert significant influences on the total supply and hence the market price. Such producers are said to exert monopoly power and when they do so, the notion of consumer sovereignty may disappear altogether. There have been attempts by the British government to control monopoly power since 1948 and the 'privatisation' policy since the early 1980s has been concerned with the removal of monopoly power from public sector oganisations. Conversely, however, the government may take the view that in a particular industry the public could best be served by a single producer and may set up an agency as the sole provider of a particular good or service. For instance, in many countries the provision of rail travel is considered to be a case for a 'natural' monopoly in order to avoid an expensive duplication of services. This requires the regulation of the quality of services and of prices charged as an essential accompaniment however.

3. Providing social goods. As the market system left to its own devices would not cater for the provision of social goods, the government has the task of deciding which of these goods (and how much) are to be produced. Such decisions as the amount of money to be spent on national defence, the police, the fire service, education etc are usually politically based. These expenditures need to be financed from taxes, and the government is essentially diverting demand away from private goods (food, clothing, hi-fi systems etc) and forcing people to purchase social goods instead.

4. Taking account of 'spillover effects'. The price system only allocates resources efficiently if the price paid in the market truly reflects the opportunity cost of producing a good. If it does not, then spillover effects must exist. This idea is considered in detail in the next chapter, but one example may suffice here. If the smoke emissions from a brickworks' chimney cause the local community to suffer the inconvenience of dirtier clothes, grimy houses and an unhealthy atmosphere, then by his actions the manufacturer is imposing a cost on the community which he does not have to meet. The government could, therefore, be justified in imposing some sort of pollution tax to counteract this cost and thereby compensate the community.

5. Providing stability in the economy. There is frequently an inability of the

market system to ensure that the total amount of demand in the economy is just at the right level to produce full employment but not so high as to push up prices and cause inflation. (Worse still, both these evils may exist at the same time.) By its ability to impose taxes and increase or decrease its own expenditure (termed fiscal control), and by its ability to manipulate interest rates and the amount of money in the economy (termed monetary control) the government is able to influence the overall level of demand in the economy.

Exercises

2.1 'A freely operating price mechanism ensures the best use of an economy's resources'. To what extent is this statement true?

2.2 Why is the British economy called a 'mixed economy'? Explain the main functions of the government in this economic system.

2.3 'Consumer sovereignty does not exist in our economy'. Is there any justification for this view?

2.4 Describe how decisions on production, consumption and distribution are made in
   a) a market economy
   b) a centrally planned economy.

(ISVA)

3

Cost-Benefit Analysis

Having considered the economic functions of government, it is now appropriate to assess one aspect of the government's economic role.

Whilst few people would argue that the government has some role to play in providing certain goods such as national defence, an adequate road network or a public education system, the extent of government involvement in certain areas – in the building industry for instance – may be open to debate. Ideas concerning the relative efficiencies of the public and private sectors may certainly affect individuals' judgements in these areas.

However, given that there is some need for the provision of certain social or public goods in society, the government frequently requires some sort of guidance on decisions to undertake specific projects or programmes of spending. This type of decision making in the public sector may be facilitated by the use of a technique termed cost-benefit analysis.

3.1 Decision making

3.1.1 Private costs and returns

A basic principle underlying the workings of the market system is that the profit motive ensures that producers use their resources to produce the types of goods that people want. A producer is in business to make as much profit as possible and this is the underlying factor influencing his investment decisions. If a brick manufacturer decides to invest in a new factory, he is concerned with the costs he has to incur and the income he can expect to receive from the extra production. These are the explicit costs and returns, of which the firm must take account and may be termed private costs and returns. They are also called internal costs and returns, as the firm includes them when making decisions on investments.

3.1.2 Social costs and benefits

There may be some costs though that result from the manufacturer's actions in setting up his factory which are imposed on others and of which he is forced to take no account. Local residents may be forced to suffer the pollution from the factory chimneys and the noise created by machinery. The scenic virtues of the area may also be reduced.

In other words, there are costs which are external to the manufacturer. When such external costs are added to the private costs, we have social costs, so called because it is society in general that bears them. In a similar way, external

15

benefits may result from the investment; if, for instance, the factory leads to new jobs being found for workers who would otherwise be unemployed, this is a social benefit for the local community.

3.2 Public Investment

A public sector investment can be regarded as being undertaken by society as a whole and so any decision should be based on the overall economic advantages and disadvantages for society. Cost-benefit analysis is an investment-appraisal technique designed to take account of all the social costs and social benefits arising from a project.

3.2.1 The use of cost-benefit analysis

A public investment project such as an urban redevelopment or the construction of a new trunk road may be considered to be economically viable if the social benefits attributable to it more than outweigh the social costs incurred. The production of such a cost-benefit 'balance sheet' is, however, often an extremely complex process fraught with many difficulties. Some of the basic problems are outlined below.

1.   The choice of benefits and costs to include. Ideally a cost-benefit analysis should take account of all the costs and benefits incurred, but in practice only the more relevant effects can be taken account of. With the construction of a new motorway, major benefits from the project, such as the reduced time taken for journeys or the reduction in congestion on existing trunk roads would be taken account of. However, a factor such as a deterioration in the visual nature of the landscape may be considered too insignificant to allow for in the analysis. The decision maker must draw the line somewhere when considering such side effects.

2.   Shadow pricing. Having decided what costs and benefits to include, the choice of values to attribute to them may prove a problem. Some items in a cost-benefit analysis may have market prices and an obvious action would be to use these values to attribute to costs and benefits. In many cases however, there may be a need for adjustment to these prices if they do not properly reflect the social costs and benefits involved. If such adjusted prices are used – or indeed if no market prices are available – a technique termed 'shadow pricing' may be used.

   A shadow price can be said to be the price which reflects the true social costs or value of a good. A good example of the use of shadow pricing exists in the situation where the labour which is used on a project may otherwise be unemployed. The opportunity cost associated with the employment of these people is therefore zero and to value the labour at the market wage would be economically incorrect. In other words it costs society nothing, in terms of output forgone, to put that labour to work.

   There are also many benefits and costs which do not have market prices and the imputation of monetary values in such cases must often involve round about methods. In some cases it may be possible to adapt prices found in similar situations where a market price exists. For instance, the benefits to local residents of a new recreation area providing free leisure facilities, could be gauged by observing the prices which people are prepared to pay to use a similar facility provided privately elsewhere.

With many collective goods though, valuation is usually made on the basis of a political decision. If people were asked how much they would be prepared to pay to have some improved facility such as a new motorway, then it could be expected that people would systematically undervalue the 'worth' to them of the expenditure. This is due to the 'free rider' principle, i.e. no-one could be excluded from using the facility and having a 'free ride', so each individual would hope that other people's 'offers' would suffice to enable the project to go ahead.

3.   Transfer payments and compensation agreements. By virtue of its ability both to raise taxes and also to spend this money on projects affecting different sectors of society, the government may be considered to have some control over the distribution of income within the community.

Taxpayers money may be spent, for instance, on a new stretch of urban motorway in Manchester, thus benefiting road users in this area. Whilst this specific group of motorists may not be asked to pay more taxes to pay for the investment, if many similar projects are undertaken the government may increase generally the taxes paid by motorists to cover the expenditure. In this way the beneficiaries from a project may be required to pay for the benefits they receive.

In a similar manner, those parties who are forced to meet the external costs resulting from a project may receive compensation for this imposition. For instance, from the construction of a new urban motorway there may result considerable noise pollution for local residents and the authorities may have to provide double glazing and other sound insulation in nearby houses. The total cost incurred in making this type of compensation payment would indicate to the government the total extent of this external cost, i.e. if £100 000 had to be spent to ensure that the local inhabitants' position was restored to its previous noise free state, then this would be the cost of 'internalising this externality'. (The money should of course come from the tax contributions of the benefiting motorists.)

Generally the beneficiaries from a project may be asked to compensate those who suffer the external costs. Direct compensation does not necessarily take place, but the government may implicitly redistribute income by its tax and compensation policies. Its objective is to ensure that overall, there is a net benefit from a project and the gainers could compensate the losers.

4.   The return on the investment. It is normally the case with any investment, be it private or public, that most of the returns or benefits from that project come over a long period of time, and this is especially true of building and civil engineering projects. For most private investments, the financial capital has to be borrowed and interest paid on this money or else the investors' own funds have to be diverted from some other use. In other words, in the latter case there is an opportunity cost associated with the capital. If the investor can make a 10% return on his money elsewhere, then he is looking for at least that return from the investment under consideration.

When the government invests in social projects on behalf of the community, the return on the investment should therefore reflect the opportunity cost of the funds used and a social opportunity cost rate of return should be used to appraise such projects. This rate being equivalent to the opportunity cost rate of return in the private sector. The reason being that money for investment by private individuals is diverted to the public sector by government taxes. An alternative view to this is that the government, with the welfare of future generations in mind, should be willing to accept a lower rate of return on its social projects involving the provision of houses, schools, roads etc than are private businessmen on their private investment, in order to ensure a sufficient provision of socially desirable investment.

3.2.2 Examples in the use of cost-benefit analysis

A look at examples of the way in which cost-benefit analysis can be used will help to illustrate some of the aforementioned points. Whilst it is a technique mainly utilised in the area of transport policy – the construction of the M1 motorway, the Victoria underground line, the Roskill Commission on a third London airport all being examples in this field – studies of urban land redevelopment projects also constitute an important area of application. The redevelopment of London's dockland and the re-siting of Covent Garden market being cases in point.

Two hypothetical examples are considered here.

Example 1   The construction of a new motorway
The possible major costs and benefits from such a project may be as follows:

Costs
Costs of constructing the motorway.
Costs of acquiring the necessary land.   } Capital outlay.
Maintenance costs of the motorway.
Costs of extra mileage incurred when vehicle drivers choose to make a faster but lengthier journey by motorway.

Benefits
Time savings made as a result of faster journeys both for those vehicle drivers who will use the motorway and those who carry on using the now less congested trunk roads.
Savings in fuel consumption and other operating costs (wear and tear) for both these groups of vehicle drivers.
Reductions in vehicle fleets, i.e. due to time savings, less vehicles are needed to make the same number of journeys from A to B.
Reductions in accidents.
Benefits for generated traffic i.e. some journeys which were not previously worth making, can now profitably be made.

The first two items in the cost section constitute the capital outlay on the project and the usual method of appraisal involves calculation of the annual benefits and the annual costs to find the net annual benefit which can then be compared with the outlay to see if a sufficiently high rate of return arises from the project.

The importance of shadow pricing in this example is obvious. Time savings, by far the largest benefits of most transport schemes, can be valued at the cost of employing the traveller in question if the time saving occurs during working time, but the appropriate valuation to attach to savings in leisure time is usually considerably lower. A price must also be attached to human life and injury, and loss of potential earnings is the main factor here. Environmental damage, especially noise, could be included in the cost section and often proves to be the most difficult cost to analyse even though it is perhaps one externality which affects a great number of people.

Example 2   An urban renewal programme
A programme of urban renewal involves the demolition of slum housing and other property in an area, most of it obviously old, so that a large area of ground is cleared, and a new set of houses, shops and other facilities and streets can be constructed.

As most of this blighted property in the older central areas of cities is often in private hands, the costs of buying up slum property, clearing the land and putting up new buildings may be greater than the value of the new properties and so such an extensive project is unprofitable for a private investor. An urban renewal scheme will only be 'profitable' for a public body taking account of the social benefits from the project.

The general costs and benefits from this type of scheme are as follows:

Costs
Costs of acquiring the existing property on the site.
Costs of preparing the site (including demolition costs).
Costs of constructing the development.
Costs of disruption to residents and to the neighbourhood during construction.

Benefits
Value of land after renewal.
Value of buildings after renewal.
Benefits from improved social conditions.

When the assessments of the market values of the old and new properties are made, shadow pricing may be necessary in a situation where the rents paid by the tenants are 'regulated' i.e. held at a level below the market rent. The most difficult tasks though, involve the valuation of the external benefits from the project. These benefits result from improved living conditions and take the form of reductions in fire hazards, less neighbourhood crime, less illness due to overcrowding and stress and possibly improved educational performances by local children. The fact that neighbouring properties to the new development may experience rises in value could be taken as an expression of the increase in welfare of the area – provided of course that this factor could be isolated from the many others affecting property values.

Overall, it may be said that the subjective nature of shadow pricing and the fact that many externalities are virtually impossible to quantify lead to a great deal of criticism of cost benefit analysis. Nevertheless, it is perhaps a valuable technique for giving the government guidance on public investment projects.

Exercises

3.1 The government is considering expenditure of a large sum of money on the expansion of a presently quite small airport close to a city in a region with a high unemployment rate.
    What are likely to be the major costs and benefits associated with the project?

3.2 The following table shows the total costs and benefits (£m) for four different urban redevelopment programmes of different magnitudes.

Programme	Total Costs	Total Benefits
A	6	14
B	14	24
C	24	32
D	36	38

Which programme should be undertaken, and why?

3.3 The government is trying to determine whether it should build a road from X to Y or whether it should build one that goes from Y to Z as well.

The benefits and costs associated with the two projects have been estimated to be:

	Road from X to Y	Road from X to Y to Z
Cost (£m)	100	140
Benefit (£m)	150	180

Which project should be undertaken, and why?

Part Two

Price Determination in the Market

4

Demand and Supply

In a freely operating market the price of any good or resource is determined by the interaction of two forces – demand and supply. Every market has these two sides to it and each side can be examined in turn.

4.1 Demand

In economics the term demand has quite a specific meaning. The desire of a consumer to purchase a good must be backed by the money or ability to pay for the good. In other words the only concern is with 'effective demand'. Most people may desire a Rolls Royce but how many of us can afford to pay for it? Our 'demand' is therefore mainly ineffective.

More specifically the demand for a product refers to the amount that consumers would be willing to buy at particular prices during a particular period.

There are obviously many factors that affect the demand for a good, but the main consideration is that of the price of that good.

4.1.1 The demand curve

It is usual to find with most goods that there is an inverse relationship between the price of the good and quantity demanded. The higher the price the less of it is demanded, whereas if the price falls existing buyers will take more and new customers will come along and buy the product.

The following example illustrates such a situation. A house builder estimates that he could sell varying numbers of houses in his development during a certain period as shown in this demand schedule:

Price (£)	Number of houses demanded
90 000	38
87 000	40
84 000	44
81 000	50
78 000	58
75 000	70

The schedule indicates how many houses would be sold if the price were at certain levels and, if we assume that intermediary points can also be estimated,

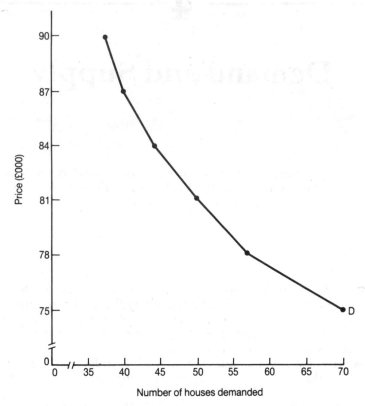

Fig. 4.1 Demand curve for houses

this same information can be depicted graphically by means of a demand curve.

Note that it is customary to measure price on the vertical axis and quantity on the horizontal axis.

If the builder decided to set a price of £84 000 he would find that he could sell 44 houses but if the price rose to £87 000 he would sell only 40. Any change in the price of the product causes a movement along – up or down – the demand curve. The demand curve itself does not move and the price change only affects the quantity demanded. From now on these movements will be referred to as contractions or extensions in demand.

4.1.2 Changes in demand conditions

Any demand curve is drawn on the assumption that no influences affect demand other than price changes, but there are many considerations which may affect the number of houses demanded at any given price. People's tastes, their incomes, the prices of other houses are just some of the factors which may change and may shift the demand curve. Factors such as these are said to determine the conditions of demand and the more important of these can be considered in turn.

a) The income level of consumers. Generally, if incomes increase, the demand curve for a good will shift to the right because more can be effectively demanded. (Similarly, a fall in income brings a shift to the left.) Our housebuilder for instance, may find that more of his potential customers are willing and now able to obtain the necessary money to demand a house.
b) The prices of other goods. It is certainly true that consumers have limited incomes and that an increase in the price of any one good will leave a consumer with less to spend on other goods. However, there are certain goods whose relative prices play an important role in determining the demand for a particular good. These are substitute goods and complementary goods.

A rented house may be seen as a substitute form of accommodation by some potential owner occupiers but if house rents were to increase then this would persuade some people to purchase a house of their own and the demand curve for the houses to purchase would shift to the right.

Alternatively, what would happen if the local tax in the area were to rise? Anyone buying a house has to buy this complementary 'product' of local authority services and when the price of providing this service rises the demand for the houses is likely to decrease.

c) Consumers' tastes. If consumers show an increasing preference for a product, then at any given price they will demand more of the good and so the demand curve will shift to the right. Vice versa, if a product appears less fashionable then the demand curve will shift to the left as consumers desire to buy less than previously.

In our example of the housebuilder, the popularity of the inclusion of such features as a patio, Georgian-style windows or a garage may influence the number which will be demanded at any particular price.

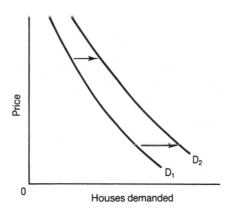

Fig. 4.2a A shift to the right of the demand curve for houses (D_1 to D_2). Possible cause; a general rise in incomes

Fig 4.2 illustrates some of these effects on the demand curve.
There are of course other factors in addition to these which are worthy of a brief mention. In our example, an expectation by potential house buyers that

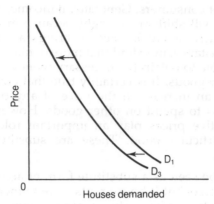

Fig. 4.2b A shift to the left of the demand curve for houses (D_1 to D_3). Possible cause; a rise in mortgage interest rates

house prices were likely to 'take-off' in the near future would produce an increase in demand now. Any change in government policy affecting house buyers, such as the removal of mortgage interest tax relief would obviously result in a shift in the demand curve.

Clearly, lots of other examples could be used to illustrate shifts in a demand curve, many being specific to particular markets.

4.2 Supply

The supply of a product refers to the amount offered for sale at particular prices during a period of time. A rise in price is likely to induce producers to expand the amount they are offering for sale while a fall in prices is likely to have the reverse effect. The reasons being that a high price will raise firms' profits and persuade them to produce more, whereas a reduction in price lessens the profit per unit and inefficient producers may be making no profit at all and be forced out of business.

There are many reasons why a particular producer is willing to supply certain quantities of a product at certain prices but the main concern is with the costs of production. In the example of the housebuilder, there may well be some areas of his site which are more difficult and expensive to develop than others due to access, drainage or site clearance problems. He will therefore, only provide more houses by using these more costly sites if he is able to obtain a higher selling price for his houses. This is shown in the following supply schedule and supply curve (Fig. 4.3).

Price (£)	Number of houses supplied
90 000	70
87 000	63
84 000	56
81 000	50
78 000	46
75 000	42

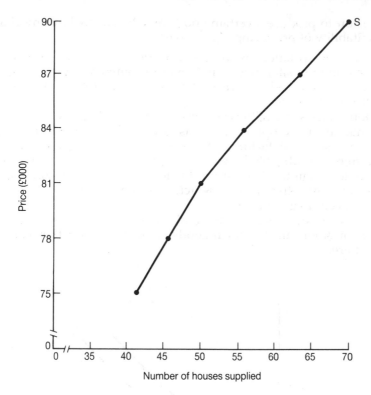

Fig. 4.3 Supply curve of houses

4.2.1 Changes in supply conditions

The supply of any product must also be affected by many considerations in addition to the price, and changes in these factors are likely to shift the position of the supply curve as indicated.

a) Technology. As technical improvements occur, it becomes possible to produce commodities more cheaply and so firms are willing to supply a given amount at a lower price than before. The supply curve will thus shift to the right. With housebuilding methods, the advent of system building in recent decades resulted in the possibility of providing cheaper housing units.

b) Input prices. The prices of the resources used to produce a commodity affect the supply curve. Increases in input prices will lower the profitability of production and reduce the amount of the commodity made available. Decreases would make it possible to produce more cheaply and cause the supply curve to shift to the right.

For the housebuilder, a rise in the price of building land, the cost of materials or construction workers' wages would all have the effect of shifting the supply curve to the left and thus bringing about a decrease in supply.

c) The prices of, and profit from, the production of alternative goods. When a supplier is able to use his resources to provide more than one type of good, his decision to produce a certain good must be affected by any changes in the profitability of producing alternatives.

Landowners, for instance, who are considering undertaking a housing development on their sites may switch over to commercial development if the price of office accommodation rises. This would, therefore, shift the supply curve for houses to the left.

Fig. 4.4 illustrates some of these effects on the supply curve.

Other changes in supply conditions are likely to result from climatic variations and seasonal factors – for instance, production in the building industry differs considerably between the summer and winter months. Government influences in the form of production subsidies, taxes on resources or tax concessions are other factors which may encourage or discourage the production of certain goods.

Again, as with our look at demand, many factors may influence the underlying conditions under which goods are supplied and they cannot all be mentioned here.

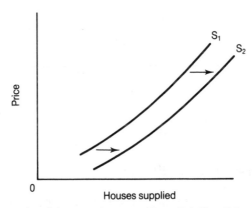

Fig. 4.4a A shift to the right of the supply curve (S_1 to S_2). Possible cause; improvements in housebuilding technology

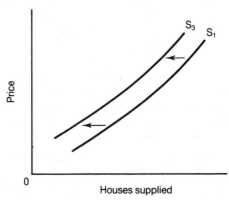

Fig. 4.4b A shift to the left of the supply curve (S_1 to S_3). Possible cause; a rise in the cost of building land

4.3 Price determination

When the two sides of a market for a product (demand and supply) are put together, it is their interaction which determines the price of the commodity.

In Fig. 4.5 the demand and supply curves for houses from our example are brought together.

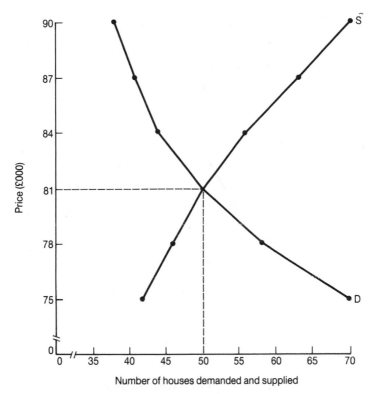

Fig. 4.5 Determination of equilibrium price

The two curves intersect at a price of £81 000 and this price is said to be the equilibrium or market price. The market is in equilibrium because at this price the number of houses which consumers wish to buy exactly equals the number which the builder is willing to provide (50 houses in either case).

In general, it is assumed that the actual price that arises in a market will be the equilibrium price. Should this not be the case at a particular time then the basic forces at work in the market will force the actual price towards the equilibrium. How this is achieved is dependent upon the initial imbalance.

Suppose that the builder had set his selling price too high – at £84 000 to begin with – he would only have found 44 potential customers for the 56 houses he would have been willing to provide, i.e. a situation of excess supply. As he is in competition with other housebuilders, there will be downward pressure on the price until it reaches £81 000. In a similar manner there is upward pressure on the price in the market if it is set too low, say £78 000, and there is a situation of excess demand, i.e. 58 houses would be demanded but the builder would be prepared to provide only 46 houses. The equilibrium price of £81 000 where the number demanded exactly equals the number supplied would again be reached.

These situations are depicted in Fig. 4.6.

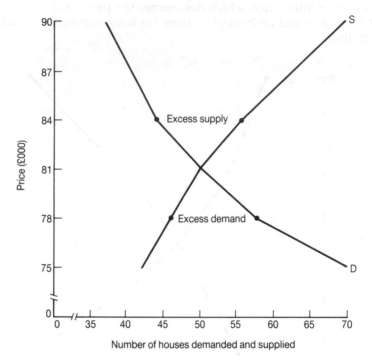

Fig. 4.6 Excess demand and supply

4.3.1 The effects of shifts in demand and supply curves

Any shift in either the demand curve or supply curve will have an effect on the equilibrium price in a market.

The demand curve for houses, for instance, would shift to the left if there happened to be a change in building society policy which made less money available for prospective house purchasers. At the initial equilibrium price of £81 000 there would now be excess supply and the builder, finding it difficult to find buyers, would be forced to lower his price. In Fig. 4.7(a) the shift in the demand curve from D to D_1 produces a new equilibrium price of £78 000. This shift in the demand curve produces a movement along the supply curve and the builder will reduce the number of houses he is now willing to build to 46.

In a similar fashion, a shift in the supply curve also affects the equilibrium price. Suppose that the builder was faced with increased costs for his building materials. The leftward shift in the supply curve (S to S_1) depicted in 4.7(b) raises the equilibrium price to £84 000 and this movement along the demand curve (i.e. a contraction in demand) means that only 44 will now be sold.

Clearly, the price in any market is subject to change whenever the forces of demand or supply themselves are affected by changing conditions.

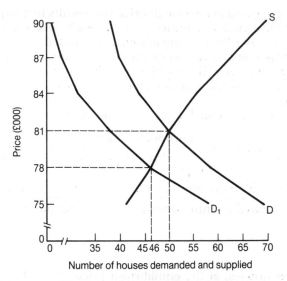

Fig. 4.7a The effect on equilibrium price of a shift in the demand curve

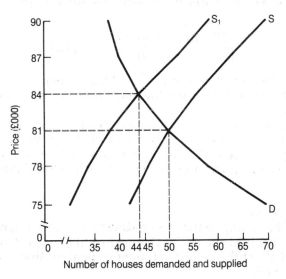

Fig. 4.7b The effect on equilibrium price of a shift in the supply curve

4.3.2 Elasticity of demand

As we have seen, the relationship between the price of a good and the amount of that good which is demanded is of prime interest in the study of any market and the measurement of the effect of any change in the price of a good on the quantity demanded is something with which economists are often concerned.

Price elasticity of demand
The quantity demanded of some commodities is fairly sensitive to changes in

the commodity's price and even a small price rise results in a large reduction in the quantity demanded. For another good though, even a relatively large increase in price may hardly alter the amount demanded.

A measure of this responsiveness of the demand for a good to a change in the price of that good is termed the (price) elasticity of demand. If the measure is standardised then the sensitivity of different goods to changes in their prices can be compared.

The following formula for such a measure can be used:

$$\text{Elasticity of demand} = \frac{\text{Proportionate change in quantity demanded}}{\text{Proportionate change in price}}$$

$$= \frac{\text{Change in quantity demanded}}{\text{Original quantity demanded}} \div \frac{\text{Change in price}}{\text{Original price}}$$

Example

Using the data on houses, at the equilibrium price of £81 000, the number of houses demanded was 50. If the price then rose to £84 000 and the number demanded fell to 44, the elasticity of demand for this price rise would be calculated as:

$$\frac{44 - 50}{50} \div \frac{84\,000 - 81\,000}{81\,000} = (-)3.24$$

(Note that even though it is normal to obtain a negative value here, the negative sign is often omitted as it is the magnitude of the elasticity with which we are mainly concerned.)

The answer obtained would of course have been different if the elasticity had been measured for a price fall from £84 000 to £81 000 (an elasticity of −3.82) because the original price and quantity would have to be altered. However, if the price changes being measured are only very small this difference should be negligible.

The value of the elasticity

It is a matter of basic importance to producers and to the government to be concerned with the effects of a price change in a market. A change in the price of a product will affect the amount of money spent on that product and thus the revenue received.

The value obtained when an elasticity is calculated is determined by the response of demand to a price change. We can broadly distinguish between three categories of value for the measure.

a) If the price elasticity is less than 1, the demand for a product is said to be price inelastic. This means that a price change produces a less than proportionate change in the quantity demanded.

Assume that a brick manufacturer raises his prices by 20% and finds that his sales only fall off by 10% – an elasticity of 0.5. The total revenue from the sale of the product to his customers (i.e. the price times the quantity demanded) will increase.

b) If the price elasticity is greater than 1, the demand for a product is said to be price elastic. The responsiveness of demand to a price change is therefore more than proportionate. Suppose that in other circumstances, the 20% increase in the price of bricks might reduce the quantity demanded by 40% – an elasticity of 2. Now the total revenue from the sales of the bricks will fall.

Figure 4.8 compares these two situations by showing the total revenue from the sale of the manufacturer's bricks when the price rises by 20% from OP to OP_1.

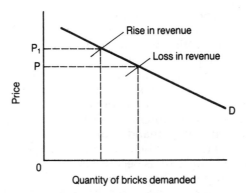

Fig. 4.8a Elastic demand. For the price rise (OP to OP_1) the reduction in revenue more than offsets the rise

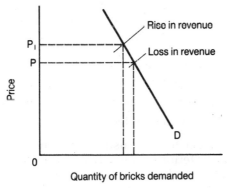

Fig. 4.8b Inelastic demand. For the price rise (OP to OP_1) the rise in revenue more than offsets the reduction

c) If the price elasticity exactly equals 1, this is termed unitary elasticity. In this case the total amount spent on a product does not alter when the price changes. So a 20% price rise would result in a 20% fall off in demand.

This last situation can be treated as a special case and the main concern of finding elasticities is to discover whether demand is elastic or inelastic.

Determinants of price elasticity of demand
Whether the elasticity of demand is high or low basically depends upon the following:

a) The existence and closeness of substitute goods. The elasticity of demand for a good is likely to be high if there are many close substitutes for that good, and the more narrowly a good is defined, the greater the number of substitutes available.

For example, if we talk about housing in general, there are not many substitutes, but if we are concerned with one particular housing development then the potential purchaser of one of these houses may have many similar options open to him.

b) The importance of the commodity in the consumer's budget. For a commodity on which the consumer spends only a very small fraction of his income, the elasticity of demand is likely to be low. If the price of salt doubled, this would be of little consequence to a consumer's budget and the change in demand consequently small. In contrast, the demand for housing is certainly more elastic because it occupies a large part of people's budgets.

c) The time period involved. As it takes time for consumers to change their spending habits, the longer the time period over which a price change persists, the easier it is for consumers to substitute one good for another and the higher the elasticity of demand. For instance, even with continual increases in the price of domestic heating oil, existing users have often been unable to switch to substitute fuels because of the high cost of conversions. New and renovated properties have, however, used relatively cheaper fuels and so, in the longer term, price rises have had greater effects on the consumption of fuel oil.

Income elasticity of demand

So far only price elasticity of demand has been examined, but another determinant of demand is consumers' income and the responsiveness of the quantity of a good demanded to changes in income is measured by the income elasticity of demand.

This measure can be defined as the proportionate change in demand divided by the proportionate change in income, and can be expressed by the formula:

$$\frac{\text{Change in quantity demanded}}{\text{Original quantity demanded}} \div \frac{\text{Change in income}}{\text{Original income}}$$

The resulting measure of elasticity is usually positive – a negative answer indicates that a good is 'inferior' as, when consumers' incomes rise, they purchase fewer units of the good.

Cross-price elasticity of demand

The quantity of a good demanded also depends upon the price of related goods. Cross-price elasticity of demand measures the effect on the demand for good X when the price of good Y changes.

It is defined as the proportionate change in the quantity of good X demanded, divided by the proportionate change in price of good Y. As a formula:

$$\frac{\text{Change in quantity of X demanded}}{\text{Original quantity of X demanded}} \div \frac{\text{Change in price of Y}}{\text{Original price of Y}}$$

Unlike the oft-ignored negative sign of price elasticity of demand, the sign of the cross elasticity of demand is an important part of the measure revealing whether the two goods being compared are substitutes or complements.

For substitute goods the measure would be positive and the larger the value the better the degree of substitution. The higher the complementarity of goods the greater the negative value of the elasticity.

Exercises

4.1 The demand and supply schedules for a certain type of metal window frame are shown below;

Quantity demanded (000s)	Price (£)	Quantity supplied (000s)	Surplus (+) or Shortage (−)
110	120	91	
105	130	92	
100	140	94	
95	150	95	
90	160	97	
80	170	99	
75	180	100	

a) Using the surplus-shortage column, indicate the equilibrium price and equilibrium quantity.

b) Suppose the producer of these frames set his selling price initially at £170. What would be the likely outcome of this action?

c) A similar type of window frame can be produced in wood. With reference to the following cross-price demand schedule, explain the relationship between the price of the metal window frame and the demand for metal and wooden frames.

Price of metal window frames (£)	Quantity of wooden window frames demanded (000s)
120	90
130	92
140	95
150	97
160	100
170	105
180	107

4.2 Explain with the aid of appropriate diagrams the likely effects of each of the following on the market for private-houses with particular reference to the level of house prices.

a) A rise in mortgage interest rates.

b) A rise in wages in the building industry.

c) A freeze on council house building.

d) A decision by the government to allow more land to be made available at low cost for private housebuilding.

4.3 Explain the likely effects on the price and quantity sold per week of good X in a given market of:

i)   a technical improvement in the production of X

ii) an increase in the incomes of consumers of X

iii) a decrease in the production costs of Y, a substitute for X.

Illustrate your answer with appropriate diagrams.

4.4 With the aid of diagrams explain as briefly as possible why an increase in income has a different effect on the demand for housing than an increase in price.

4.5 'If we observe a rise in the price of a good, accompanied by a rise in the amount bought, then the demand curve for that good must be upward sloping'. (B.J. McCormick et al. *Introducing Economics*).
Discuss this proposition in the light of your knowledge of the theory of demand.

(ISVA)

4.6 The following demand schedule shows the number of flats in an area which would be rented at various monthly rent levels.

Rent (£)	Number of flats
140	80
160	70
180	50
200	40
220	30
240	20

If the going rent is £160, what is the elasticity of demand for;
a) a fall of £20 in the monthly rent?
b) a rise in the rent of £40?

4.7 If the suppliers of a certain building material would be willing to put the following quantities on the market at the particular prices

Price (£)	10	9	8	7	6
Quantity supplied (units)	280	225	170	130	110

Calculate the elasticity of supply
a) for a price fall from £10 to £9
b) for a price rise from £6 to £8.

4.8 Economists refer to the demand for housing as being price inelastic but income elastic.
Distinguish between and explain these two terms.

(ISVA)

4.9 a) Briefly explain the terms:
   i)   own price elasticity
   ii) cross price elasticity
   iii) income elasticity.
   b) For a normal good the own price and income elasticity of demand are found to be respectively −1.5 and +1.0. What are the implications of these values for the:
   i) short-run pricing policy of the firm supplying the good?
   ii) market for the good in the long-run?

(ISVA)

5

Interference in the Market

The basic purpose of the government's intervention in the operations of the price system and the form that this interference takes have already been mentioned (in Chapter 2). An important aspect of this involvement is the government's use of fiscal (i.e. concerned with government taxation and expenditure) policy and the effects of expenditure taxes imposed on goods and services.

There may be many varied reasons why the government needs to raise taxes in order to finance its own expenditure, and indirect (expenditure) taxes constitute an important proportion of this money. Also, the government may have other policy objectives which may be met by the use of such taxes. For instance, a tax on cigarettes or a subsidy (i.e. a negative tax) on milk may both be socially desirable for health reasons.

5.1 The effects of expenditure taxes and subsidies on supply

When the government places a tax on a commodity the situation in which the producer finds himself, is that the tax must be considered to be a 'cost' of supplying the good which he will pass on to the consumers, if he is able. Before looking at an example it may help to distinguish between a specific tax and an 'ad valorem' tax. A specific tax is simply a 'per-unit' tax, i.e. the same amount of tax is charged on each unit, whereas an 'ad valorem' tax is levied as a proportion of the value of the good.

The effects of such taxes can be illustrated by reference to the example on houses used in Chapter 4 (Fig. 4.3). The schedule showed the relationship between the price of houses and the number which the developer would be willing to provide. If there is no tax on the sale of houses, the developer receives the full market price, but if a tax is imposed he receives this market price less the amount of the tax. So, as the producer wishes to obtain the same amount of money from each house as he did before the tax, his asking price for each house will have to rise by the full amount of the tax. In other words, his supply curve must move vertically upwards by the full amount of the tax.

5.1.1 A specific tax

Suppose that the government put a tax of £3000 on the sale of a new house regardless of the selling price. The developer would now be willing to sell any house only at a price of £3000 above his previous asking price. His original and new supply schedules are given below:

Original supply schedule

Price (£)	Number of houses supplied	Price after the £3000 sales tax is levied (£)
90 000	70	93 000
87 000	63	90 000
84 000	56	87 000
81 000	50	84 000
78 000	46	81 000
75 000	42	78 000

The resulting supply curves are shown in Fig. 5.1.

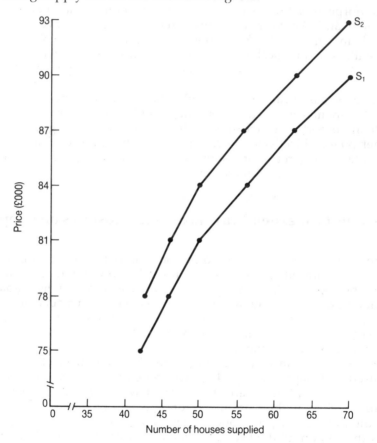

Fig. 5.1 The effect on the supply curve for houses of a sales tax of £3000

The original supply curve (S_1) moves vertically upwards by £3000 at all points to form a new supply curve (S_2).

Conversely, if the government decided that it had a social obligation to give a subsidy of £3000 on every house sale, then the supply curve would move vertically downwards in a similar fashion.

5.1.2 An 'ad valorem' tax

Instead of levying a straight per unit tax, the tax might be expressed as a percentage of the value of each house. For instance a 4% levy on the sale price of each house would produce the following changes in the supply schedule:

Original supply schedule		
Price	*Number of*	*Price after the 4%*
(£)	*houses supplied*	*sales tax is levied (£)*
90 000	70	93 600
87 000	63	90 480
84 000	56	87 360
81 000	50	84 240
78 000	46	81 120
75 000	42	78 000

i.e. New price = Old price + (4% × Old price).

In the case of the specific tax the new supply curve moved upwards in a parallel fashion, but the 'ad valorem' tax obviously has a greater absolute effect when the price is higher, as illustrated in Fig. 5.2.

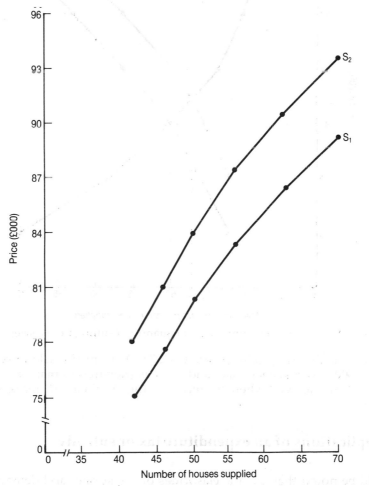

Fig. 5.2 The effect on the supply curve for houses of a 4% sales tax

5.2 Effects on market price and amount sold

When a tax is imposed on a commodity, the market price can generally be expected to rise and the amount sold reduced.

Referring to the case of a specific tax of £3000 on house sales, if the demand curve were plotted on the same diagram as the original and new supply curves the market price would rise by £1200 from £81 000 to £82 200, and the number of houses sold would go down by 3 from 50 to 47. (See Fig. 5.3).

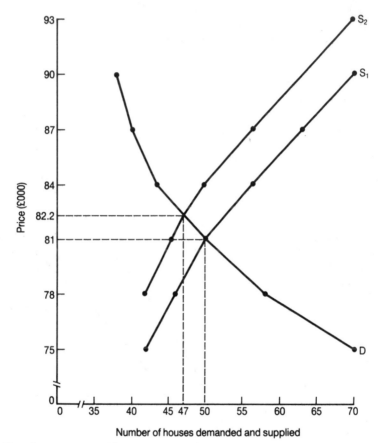

Fig. 5.3 The change in equilibrium price and quantity resulting from a sales tax of £3000

In other words, the producer receives £79 200 from the sale of each house after the £3000 tax has been paid, and so he is prepared to make fewer houses available, than he was when he received the original full market price of £81 000.

5.3 Implications of an expenditure tax or subsidy

It should be noted that it is the elasticities of the supply and demand curves, which between them determine the rise in price to the buyers, the reduction in the number of houses sold and the revenue (i.e. the tax times the number of houses sold) which the government receives. Generally, the more inelastic is the market, the more money the government is likely to raise without seriously affecting the number of houses sold. It would only be in such a situation that the government would be likely to introduce such a tax to raise substantial revenue.

The effect of a subsidy would be the opposite to that of a tax. A subsidy on the sale of a house would be motivated by a desire on the part of the government to reduce the price of such an essential good to house buyers and also to ensure that builders were given the incentive to make more houses available.

Exercises

5.1 The following figures show the demand and supply schedules for a certain type of double glazing unit.

Price (£)	Number of units demanded	Number of units supplied
160	820	590
170	750	600
180	690	620
190	650	650
200	610	690
210	560	740

a) Plot the demand and supply curves and find the equilibrium price.
b) As part of an energy saving programme, the government decides to subsidise the selling price of the units by £25 per unit. Show the new supply curve on the diagram and hence estimate the new equilibrium price.

5.2 Given the following schedule of demand for natural gas, indicate by the use of a diagram
i)   the new market price
ii) the new quantity traded
iii) the supplier's net receipts (i.e. net of tax)
if a specific tax of 10p per unit is levied.

Price (pence per unit)	15	20	25	30	35
Quantity demanded (000 units)	100	90	85	70	60
Quantity supplied (000 units)	60	70	80	90	100

(ISVA)

5.3 a) Outline the distinction between an 'ad valorem' tax and a specific tax.
b) The following schedule indicates the quantities of a commodity that will be demanded and supplied at various selected prices.

Price (£)	2	3	4	5	6	7	8	9	10
Quantity demanded (units)	88	82	76	70	64	58	52	46	40
Quantity supplied (units)	48	52	56	60	64	68	72	76	80

If a specific tax of £5 is levied, indicate the after tax
i)   market price
ii) quantity traded
iii) total tax revenue.

(ISVA)

5.4 The schedule given below indicates the demand for and supply of two-bedroomed furnished accommodation at different weekly rents for an urban area in Southern England.

Demand	57	68	84	105	132
Supply	79	68	57	51	46
Rent (£)	100	80	65	54	44

If legislation governing furnished accommodation restricts rents to £65 per week, what situation will arise in the market?

(ISVA)

5.5 What would be the likely effect of imposing a maximum price for a commodity below that freely determined in the market? How would it affect your conclusions if the maximum price was set above market price?

(ISVA)

5.6 With the aid of a diagram, identify and explain the following with respect to the imposition of a commodity tax
a) consumers' tax burden
b) producers' tax burden
c) total tax revenue
d) market price to consumers per unit after the imposition of the tax
e) producers' net of tax price per unit.

(ISVA)

Part Three
The Economics of the Firm

6

Costs of Production and Market Structures

A fundamental principle of the price system is that a producer responds to the profit motive. Quite simply it is the profit which he makes that induces him to produce a good.

Profit is the difference between the revenue obtained when a producer sells his output and the costs involved in producing and distributing that output.

In other words:

$$\text{Profit} = \text{Revenue} - \text{Costs}$$

To consider the fundamental notion of profit, it is therefore necessary to look at the behaviour of costs.

Before looking at types of cost in detail, a distinction must be made between the economic concepts of the *'short term'* and the *'long term'*. The importance being that it is only in the short term that a producer is faced with a situation where certain of his factors of production are fixed in supply i.e. he has a fixed amount of plant and equipment and is therefore restricted in his production capacity. In the long term though, there are no such constraints and capacity can be varied according to the producer's needs.

An example may help to clarify this distinction. If a plant producing tiles were to take on an extra fifty workers this would be a short term adjustment. If an extension were to be added to the same plant and extra equipment installed to allow an extra production run, this would be a long term adjustment.

6.1 Costs in the short term

A producer's costs can basically be split into two categories. Those costs which remain constant with changes in the level of output are the fixed costs of production, whereas those which vary as a producer increases his output are termed variable costs.

6.2 Fixed costs

These costs are often referred to as overheads or indirect costs and are those costs which have to be met regardless of the level of production. They generally consist of rent, rates, insurance, interest charges and the costs of indirect labour not directly concerned with production, i.e. those concerned with administration.

6.3 Variable costs

When a firm is producing its output though, it incurs some costs which increase as the level of output rises. The cost of the materials involved is an obvious example, and energy costs to provide power for machinery, labour costs of production workers and the costs of transporting materials and goods also come under this heading.

6.4 Normal profit as a cost of production

The costs mentioned so far are explicit costs, in the sense that a firm has to make payments to hire labour, buy materials, rent land etc. To produce any good, however, another factor of production not yet considered, is the enterprise required to organise production.

Any entrepreneur or businessman who puts his own resources to productive use expects to receive at least a 'normal profit' which is equivalent to the opportunity cost of using these resources elsewhere. This 'normal profit' must be considered in economic terms to be a cost which has to be met by the firm. As an example, suppose that a joiner sets up business for himself instead of working for his local direct works department. If he could earn £200 per week from this employment, then he will expect to take at least £200 per week for himself from his business plus an extra amount to cover the element of risk inherent in any business venture. This profit is the minimum reward needed to persuade the entrepreneur to bother to undertake production.

6.5 Costs and output

To examine the relationship between production costs and output in some detail, it is important to distinguish between different measures or cost. These are:

a) *Total cost.*   This is self-explanatory and consists of the sum of fixed and variable costs at each level of output.
b) *Average cost.*   This is the total cost divided by the number of units produced, i.e. the unit-cost.
c) *Marginal cost.*   This is the additional cost of producing one more unit of output.

As we shall see, these three measures of cost are important ones for economic analysis. They can be explained by reference to a simple example.

Imagine a company producing only one product – standardised ceramic tiles. The tiles can only be produced in batches of one thousand and the capacity of the firm's plant is such that it is able to produce a maximum of seven batches per day. The costs incurred in producing varying numbers of batches are shown in Table 6.1.

Table 6.1 Costs of production

1 Output (Number of batches)	2 Total Fixed Cost £	3 Total Variable Cost £	4 Total Cost £	5 Average Fixed Cost £	6 Average (Total) Cost £	7 Marginal Cost £
0	200	–	200	–	–	
1	200	380	580	200	580	380
2	200	600	800	100	400	220
3	200	760	960	66	320	160
4	200	880	1080	50	270	120
5	200	1040	1240	40	248	160
6	200	1360	1560	34	260	320
7	200	1780	1980	28	282	420

Two points need to be made concerning the relationship between sets of data. The total cost figures in column 4 consist of the total fixed and total variable cost figures added together. This is illustrated in Fig. 6.1. The marginal cost figures are found by simply subtracting the total cost figure for the nth unit of output from the total cost for the $(n-1)^{th}$ unit, e.g. the total cost of producing three batches is £960 and this total increases by £(1080 − 960) = £120, when a fourth batch is produced. Fig. 6.2 shows the relationship between the average and marginal cost curves drawn from the data.

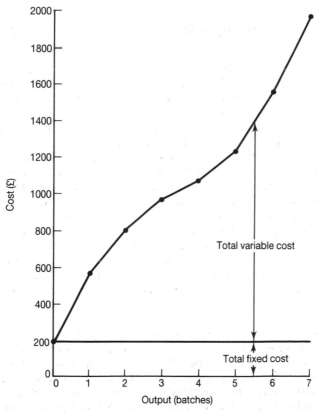

Fig 6.1 Total costs of production

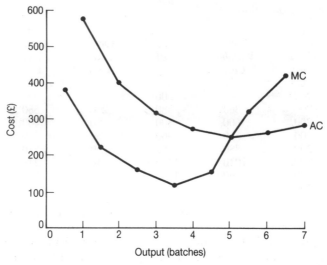

Fig. 6.2 Average Cost (AC) and Marginal Cost (MC)

6.6 The law of diminishing returns

From the table of costs, it can be seen that the marginal cost of producing extra batches of tiles falls at first but then eventually rises. These changes in marginal cost also produce an average cost curve which must begin to rise as soon as the marginal cost curve intersects it.

The reason for this initial fall and ensuing rise in average and marginal cost is explained in economic analysis by the *law of diminishing returns* (or law of variable proportions). In the example we are assuming that the producer is only able to vary one factor of production (the number of workers) and the other factors of production (especially capital such as the machinery and buildings) are fixed. As the firm initially hires more labour, each additional worker increases the firm's output by a considerable amount mainly due to the workers' specialisation in certain jobs. Eventually though, as the labour force grows the machinery starts to be utilised to almost full capacity and by hiring extra workers the firm adds little to its total production. An extra worker may perhaps be forced to spend most of his time working on odd jobs without being very productive. In economic terms, the proportion of fixed factors relative to variable factors becomes too small to produce efficiently – an extra or bigger plant is called for.

The principles of increasing and diminishing returns to scale are therefore both illustrated in the example. Assuming that each worker costs the same amount to employ, then the firm finds that the *marginal product* (i.e. increase in output) associated with employing an initial number of workers (up to ON in Fig. 6.3) is increasing and this is referred to as a situation of increasing returns to scale. Conversely, as the firm employs beyond ON workers, the marginal product is falling and this results in diminishing returns to scale.

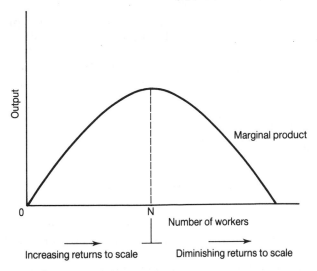

Fig. 6.3 Returns to scale

6.7 Production decisions

To determine how a producer chooses his most profitable output it is necessary to analyse the revenue he obtains from the sale of his products as well as the costs involved in producing them.

Total revenue can be defined as the income the producer receives from his sales and is calculated by multiplying the unit selling price of his product by the number of units sold. The price he receives for his good depends upon conditions in the market in which he operates.

Economic theory indicates that several distinct forms of market can exist and these different situations may be analysed separately.

6.8 Types of market

It is usual to categorise markets with respect to the number of suppliers in the market. A whole spectrum of situations may thus exist, ranging from a single producer (or monopolist) at one extreme, to a market in which thousands of producers are competing with each other. However, it is possible to make a simplified classification consisting of four types of market as follows:

a) *Perfect competition*   This exists when there are a large number of relatively small producers in an industry and each is producing a virtually identical product.

b) *Monopolistic competition*   Again there are many producers but each one's product is seen to be slightly different from his competitors' due perhaps to brand-naming or packaging.

c) *Oligopoly*	Only a few producers supply the product and a higher degree of differentiation exists than in the previous situation.
d) *Monopoly*	There is only a single producer of a particular good.

In theory all these market conditions could occur, but in practice virtually all industries fall into the middle two categories, and one of the two extreme situations, perfect competition, rarely, if ever exists.

6.9 Perfect and imperfect markets

A perfectly competitive market is an unrealistic proposition because the conditions for its existence are particularly restrictive. For a perfect market to exist, all the following conditions must be met:

1.   A large number of buyers and sellers in competition, and each buyer or seller so small that by his own actions he is unable to affect the market price. As each producer is only producing a minute fraction of the industry's output, even if he doubled his output or dropped out of business altogether it would not be significant.

2.   Each seller's good is indistinguishable from his competitors' products as far as buyers are concerned. Any buyer's choice of product is consequently based solely on price as there are no quality differences.

3.   There is perfect knowledge on the part of every buyer and seller with regard to the price being asked by each seller and so no price difference can exist; any seller asking a higher price than his competitors will soon lose all his customers.

4.   It is an easy matter for buyers and sellers to enter the market or to leave it. The product must accordingly be one which can be produced in a relatively short period of time and the producer does not need to tie up a lot of expensive capital and equipment in the process. The resources he requires must also be easy to obtain.

If even just one of these conditions does not hold then a market cannot be described as perfect.

At the other extreme, a true monopoly rarely exists in the private sector, and so in the real world imperfect competition of some degree is the norm. In the building industry, for instance, the largest contractors in the industry each account for only a few per cent of the total market for new construction, and the total private sector of the industry consists of tens of thousands of firms.

In certain specialist sectors of the industry though, where a high degree of technology is required, such as the construction of nuclear power stations, it is to be expected that an oligopoly exists as only a few firms are capable of undertaking such a project.

6.9.1 Output decisions in a perfectly competitive industry

Even though no real life industry meets all the requirements of perfect competition, there are perhaps two good reasons for considering the notion. Firstly, insight can be gained into the workings of certain industries, including some sectors of the construction industry, which may closely resemble perfect competition. Secondly, the ideas thrown up by perfect competition can act as a norm by which to judge other market situations, especially as an optimum allocation of resources arises from perfect competition because, as will be seen, every firm is producing at minimum unit cost.

In a perfectly competitive industry, no single producer is able to influence significantly the overall market price and so we say that each individual firm is a price taker and has to accept the equilibrium market price which is set by total supply and demand for the industry's product, as shown in Fig. 6.4.

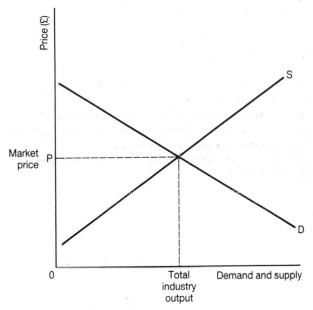

Fig. 6.4 Market equilibrium under perfect competition

The equilibrium market price is OP and the individual firm will sell all the units of output that it can put on the market profitably at that price. This effectively means that the firm is faced with a horizontal (perfectly elastic) demand curve for its product at a price of OP as in Fig. 6.5.

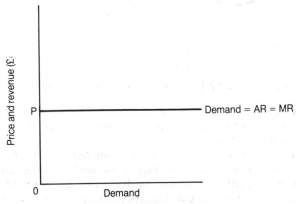

Fig. 6.5 The demand curve facing the individual firm

The line across from point P on the price axis must also be the firm's *average revenue* (AR) and *marginal revenue* (MR) curve. AR is defined as the total revenue received by the firm divided by the number of units and as every unit is being sold for £OP, price and AR must be the same. The firm's MR is the extra revenue received from the sale of one more unit and as the sale of every additional unit brings in £OP, this must also be the same as the price. As a simple example, if the market price of a product is £10 and 20 units are sold, the total revenue (TR) is £200. When an extra unit is sold, TR rises to £210 and so AR = £210/21 = £10, and MR = £(210 − 200) = £10.

If the costs of production which we looked at previously are now introduced, we can consider the overall situation for the firm.

6.9.2 The objective of the firm

Whilst there may be many reasons why a firm is in business, perhaps the most rational assumption to make is that a producer's overall aim is to make as large a profit as possible. In other words he is a *profit maximiser* and regardless of the market conditions in which he operates, we assume that this is the main consideration determining his output decision.

The usual cost curves are shown together with the perfectly competitive firm's revenue curves in Fig. 6.6.

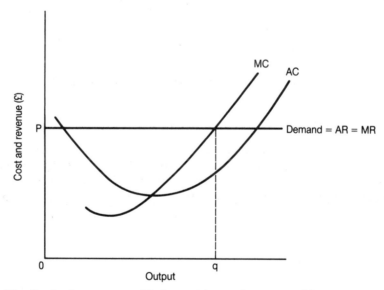

Fig. 6.6 The firm's short-run equilibrium under perfect competition

To achieve its objective, the firm produces at the point where the (upward rising) marginal cost curve cuts the marginal revenue curve. This gives a profit maximising output of Oq units.

This is not the same as the firm's *optimum output* which is that level of production where it has lowest average cost and may be considered to be operating most efficiently. The reason is that even if the firm's average cost is increasing, it pays to produce extra units as long as the marginal revenue is greater than the marginal cost and the firm is adding to its total profit. There is no incentive to produce any units beyond Oq because any extra unit adds more to costs than it does to revenue.

The firm in this situation may be able to make a fairly high level of profit. The producer includes his normal profit as a cost of production and any extra profit above that is termed *supernormal* or *abnormal profit*. The total amount of supernormal profit being made can therefore be shown in Fig. 6.7 as the difference between the firm's average revenue and average cost curves when the output of Oq is produced. Supernormal profit per unit of output is £RP.

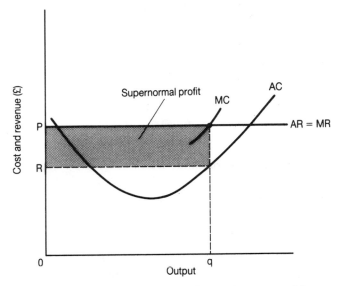

Fig. 6.7 Supernormal profit in the short-run under perfect competition

6.9.3 Perfect competition in the long-run

If this firm is typical of the other firms in the industry with regard to the large profits being made then new firms are going to be attracted to the market to 'take a slice of the action'.

This has the effect of shifting the industry supply curve to the right from S to S_1 (Fig. 6.8) and the market price consequently falls from OP to OP_1.

The individual firm is now forced to accept a lower price for its product, and as Fig. 6.9 indicates, the eventual long-run equilibrium arises when the firm's supernormal profits are totally removed and the firm is just able to cover its costs by producing its optimum output of Oq_1.

If the price were to fall below the level where the firm is able to cover its costs then the firm would not be able to carry this loss for long – the producer may carry on for a short while as long as he could at least cover his wages, raw materials and other variable costs – and would go out of business. This would have the effect of decreasing the industry supply and the market price would rise again to the level of minimum average cost for the remaining firms.

Due to the fact that perfect competition encourages efficiency and firms tend to produce their optimum output, it is a type of market which is often encouraged by governments. We can now briefly focus on other forms of market arrangements to consider how they compare with the perfect market.

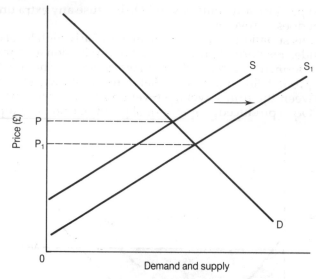

Fig. 6.8 Market price in the long-run under perfect competition

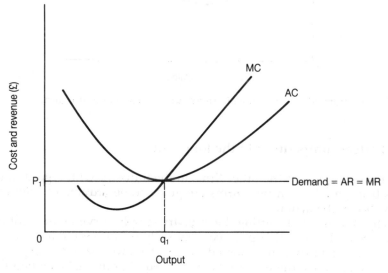

Fig. 6.9 The firm's long-run equilibrium under perfect competition

6.10 Imperfect competition

Any market is imperfect if it does not meet all the necessary conditions of a perfect market. If any firm in the industry is able to control the market price of the product in any way, then perfect competition does not exist. Three such categories of industrial situation – monopolistic competition, oligopoly and monopoly – have already been identified and the major distinction between the three types is the degree of concentration in the industry.

Under conditions of monopolistic competition, there tends to be a large number of competing firms, but some of the firms may have been able to carve out a significant share of the market for themselves and a certain degree of brand loyalty may exist amongst consumers. These dominant firms are able, within limits, to raise the price of their products and still retain some share of the market. Monopolistic competition can be thought of as a compromise between perfect competition and monopoly.

A firm may be able to earn supernormal profits for the short period during which other firms are unable to enter the industry. This is demonstrated in Fig. 6.10.

The price of the product is OP, but the unit cost only OR. The supernormal profit is RP and will be earned by the firm until new firms enter the industry.

Even though new firms are producing differentiated products the demand for this firm's product will be lower at each price. The average revenue curve will move to the left until the supernormal profits disappear as shown in Fig. 6.11.

The firm now produces an output of Oq_1 which is sold for OP_1 per unit. As the unit cost is also OP_1, no supernormal profit is earned.

In this long-run position, production is not carried out at the level of minimum unit cost and there is excess capacity in the industry because each firm is not producing its optimum output.

In this sense monopolistic competition represents a less efficient market situation than perfect competition.

6.10.1 Relationship between average and marginal revenue curves

One major difference between the circumstances of the firm in monopolistic competition and those facing the perfectly competitive firm is that the former is

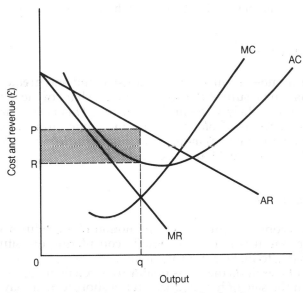

Fig. 6.10 The firm under monopolistic competition in the short-run

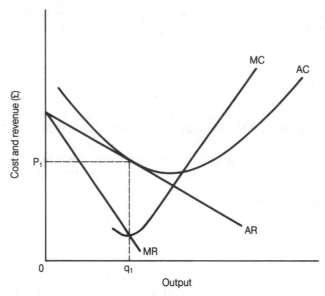

Fig. 6.11 Monopolistic competition in the long-run

faced with a downward sloping demand curve and the average revenue and marginal revenue curves are quite separate. The fact that the firm is not faced with a perfectly elastic demand curve is due to this firm's degree of control in setting the price. The reason for the difference between the firm's AR and MR curves is apparent if a hypothetical demand schedule is considered.

Quantity demanded (units)	1	2	3	4	5	6
Price (AR) (£)	10	9	8	7	6	5
Total Revenue (£)	10	18	24	28	30	30
Increase in revenue (MR) (£)		8	6	4	2	0

The MR curve will lie below the AR curve when these figures are plotted.

6.10.2 Market control

The fewer the number of firms in an industry and the greater the extent to which the firms can be sure of obtaining a certain share of the market, the more abundant are profits likely to be in the industry. This is especially true in the more extreme situations of oligopoly and monopoly and the concern of the government with the development of monopolistic control by one or a few firms in an industry is considered in Chapter 8.

6.10.3 Profit and loss

Whilst the main concern here is with the notion of a producer who wishes to maximise his profit, it is also worth briefly considering the situation where a producer is unable to make any profit at all.

What if a producer finds that he is unable to cover all his costs by the revenue he obtains from the sale of his product? In the short-term it may be viable for a producer to carry on production for a period as long as he is able to cover the variable costs of production (i.e. pay his workers wages, cover material costs. etc). But in the long-term this situation will be unsustainable with accumulating fixed costs forcing the producer out of business.

6.11 The significance of breaking even

As a final point involving the cost structure of a firm it is important to consider that a producer's initial concern may be to ensure that his sales revenue at least covers his basic costs.

Due to the fact that some of a firm's costs are fixed, it must suffer losses until a given break-even volume of sales is reached. If the fixed costs comprise a significant part of total costs then it is more important that a producer operates as near to full capacity as possible. The notion of break-even can best be considered by reference to a simple example.

Suppose that producer X has fixed costs of £50 000 and that variable costs are £1.50 per unit of output. The selling price of his product is £2 per unit.

(For the sake of simplicity, it is assumed that variable costs per unit are constant.)

His break-even output can be calculated from the following formula:

$$\text{Break-even point} = \frac{\text{Total fixed costs}}{\text{Selling price per unit} - \text{Variable cost per unit}}$$

In this example, we have $\dfrac{50\,000}{2.00 - 1.50} = 100\,000$ units.

This can be presented graphically in Fig. 6.12 as a break-even chart.

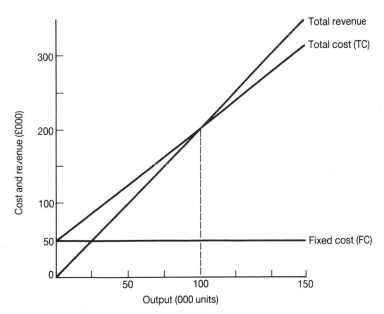

Fig. 6.12 Break-even chart

A break-even chart can also give an indication of a producer's ability to cope with adverse economic conditions or to take advantage of a boom in the demand for his product. In Fig. 6.13 producer X's break-even situation is compared to that of producer Y who sells his product for the same price but has a different cost structure. His fixed costs are £30 000 and his variable cost per unit is £1.70. The break-even output for producer Y is therefore also 100 000 units i.e.

$$\frac{30\,000}{2.00 - 1.70} = 100\,000$$

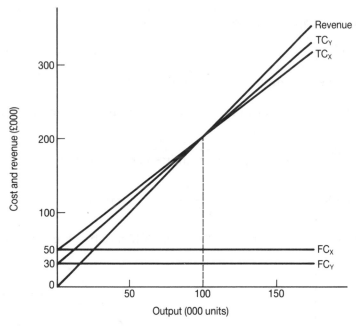

Fig. 6.13 Break-even comparison for producers X and Y

Should demand for each producer's product temporarily fall to a level of 50 000 units, both would be making a loss but producer Y would be able to weather the storm more easily with his lower level of fixed costs (Producer X's loss = £25 000; producer Y's loss = £15 000). With a high level of demand though, say 150 000 units for each product, producer X's low unit variable costs enable him to make the higher profit (Producer X's profit = £25 000; producer Y's profit = £15 000).

Exercises

6.1   Complete the following table which relates to the costs associated with the construction of various numbers of detached houses on a particular site.

Number of houses	Total Cost £000	Average Cost £000	Marginal Cost £000
0	0	–	–
1	64	–	–
2			60
3	–	58	
4	–	–	54
5	290	–	
6	–	60	–

Explain the behaviour of the marginal cost schedule in this example.

6.2 The information below relates to a firm producing vinyl floor tiles.

Output (000)	0	1	2	3	4	5	6	7	8	9
Total revenue (£)	–	100	200	300	400	500	600	700	800	900
Total cost (£)	200	280	300	340	360	370	380	420	500	640

a) What is the price of the product per unit?
b) What are the firm's fixed costs?
c) At what output does the firm maximise profits?
d) At what output level is cost at minimum per unit?

(ISVA)

6.3 An office developer finds that as building height increases the market value of the floor space created on a particular site increases less than proportionately compared with capital development costs. This is shown in the table below.

Numbers of floors	1	2	3	4	5
Capital cost per floor (£000)	40	40	40	40	40
Value of total floor space created (£000)		240	296	348	388	412

What height will the developer aim to build and why?

(ISVA)

6.4 You are consulted by a builder who estimates that for the construction of houses on a particular site his costs will be as follows.

Houses to be built	1	2	3	4	5
Total variable costs (£)	48 000	88 000	148 000	224 000	340 000

Total fixed costs: £40 000 (already incurred).

a) If each house can be sold for £60 000 advise the builder on his best course of action.
b) What would be your advice if the maximum price he can sell each house for is £40 000?

(ISVA)

6.5 A firm must decide which of two alternative goods to produce. Product X involves an outlay on fixed costs of £500 000 per annum, there is a variable cost per unit of £10 and selling price is £15. Product Y has fixed costs of £750 000 per annum, a variable cost per unit of £8 and a selling price of £14.

a) Show the break-even output for each product on break-even charts.
b) If the demand for both of these products is likely to be growing in the future, explain which product should prove most profitable.

6.6 A manufacturer produces 45 000 mobile units and sells them at £400 per unit. His fixed costs amount to £6 000 000 and variable costs £11 000 000.

a) Determine his break-even points.
b) If he raises his profit target by £400 000 show his break-even volume in

each case where he realises the increased profit by:
  i)   increasing his unit selling price.
  ii) cutting his fixed costs.
  iii) cutting his variable costs.

6.7 The conditions under which small jobbing builders maximise profits are identical to those for minimising loss. Briefly explain.

(ISVA)

6.8 'A firm wishing to maximise its profits will aim to produce and sell that output at which its marginal cost and marginal revenue are equal'.
With the help of an appropriate diagram, explain this statement. Do you think that the statement needs qualifying in any way? If so, how?

6.9 Giving short explanations and/or diagrams in each case, indicate whether the statements below regarding the competitive structure of a market are true or false:
  a) in a highly competitive market, in the long run only normal profits are earned.
  b) unless forced to charge a price equal to marginal cost, a pure monopolist can always earn abnormal profits.
  c) a monopolist will always charge a higher price and produce a lower output than a highly competitive supplier.
  d) a highly competitive producer is a price-taker.

(ISVA)

6.10 From the following information, calculate
  a) average revenue
  b) marginal revenue

Total sales (000s)	20	35	55	80	110	150
Total revenue (£000s)	40	70	110	160	220	300

What type of market competitive structure is implied by the statistics given above?

(ISVA)

7

Factor Markets

The general principle that the prices of goods and services can be determined by the interaction of demand and supply has been established already. This same principle holds good for the prices of the factors of production that firms require in order to produce their outputs, and an analysis similar to that applied to consider the market for consumer goods can be used to view the determination of wages and other factor prices.

7.1 Derived demand

Demand in the factor market comes from producers who require the services of the factors of production. These factors are normally demanded, not for their own sake directly but instead to produce something else, i.e. goods and services. This type of demand is termed *derived demand*. Thus there is, for example, a derived demand for land on which houses can be built and for labour and equipment to construct the houses.

The usefulness of a factor to a producer in enabling him to produce his good or service therefore determines his demand for that factor.

7.2 Fixed and variable factors of production

On the supply side, the availability of factors to the producer may vary significantly, dependent especially upon the period of time under consideration. The quantity of some resources that a producer requires might be varied easily even in the short term. For instance, a company that wishes to expand its unskilled workforce may have little trouble in obtaining the extra workers. In spite of employment legislation and trade unionism, in economic theory labour is still usually considered to be the most variable factor of production.

In any type of production process, there are inevitably some resources which the firm has difficulty in varying. The amounts of plant and buildings available take time to adjust and the factors capital and land are taken to be fixed factors in the short-term production process.

The theory of factor price determination that follows is based on the notion that a factor of production is totally variable, e.g. a producer can increase or reduce his labour force as he wishes. In the analysis labour is taken as the variable factor but in less usual situations the analysis could apply to any of the other factors.

7.3 Marginal productivity theory

As a basic principle, it is assumed that a firm will only hire an extra unit of labour as long as the extra 'benefit' the firm obtains is greater than the extra labour costs incurred.

This 'benefit' is usually measured in terms of the revenue that comes into the firm from the sale of its product. Thus the producer is concerned with the *marginal revenue product of labour* (MRPL) which can be defined as the increase in output that occurs when an extra worker is employed (the marginal physical product) multiplied by the selling price of that output.

This concept is easily explained by the use of a simple example. A firm which has a fixed amount of plant and equipment can add to its total output only by taking on extra workers. If the firm is selling its product in a perfectly competitive market and obtains £15 for every unit that it sells, the marginal revenue product of each extra unit of labour can be calculated as in Table 7.1.

Table 7.1 The marginal revenue product of labour

Number of workers	Total product (units)	Marginal product (units)	Price per unit of product (£)	Marginal Revenue Product of Labour (£)
1	20	20	15	300
2	45	25	15	375
3	73	28	15	420
4	99	26	15	390
5	122	23	15	345
6	142	20	15	300
7	158	16	15	240
8	169	11	15	165
9	174	5	15	75
10	174	0	15	0

Initially, the marginal product increases as a second and third worker are employed but falls more and more with the introduction of the fourth and successive workers. The reasons for this situation were discussed in the previous chapter where the law of diminishing returns was explained.

We have already seen that any firm wishing to maximise its profits will produce that output which equates marginal revenue with marginal cost. In a similar manner the firm's employment decisions are based on the equality of the marginal revenue product of labour with the marginal wage cost, which is the extra cost incurred when one more worker is employed.

Suppose that this firm finds that the employment of any extra worker adds £240 to its total costs, i.e. the wages paid plus other expenses such as insurance, superannuation contributions etc. In other words, the market for labour is a perfect one. The firm is therefore willing to add to its workforce as long as the employment of an extra worker increases total revenue by at least £240. This means the equilibrium number of workers is seven, as shown in Fig. 7.1.

What would happen in this case if, say, owing to successful wage negotiation, the wage rate is forced up to £300?

The effect would be that the firm would now find it worthwhile to employ only six workers and one worker would become redundant. This unemployment could be alleviated though, if the MRPL were to increase (to $MRPL_1$ in

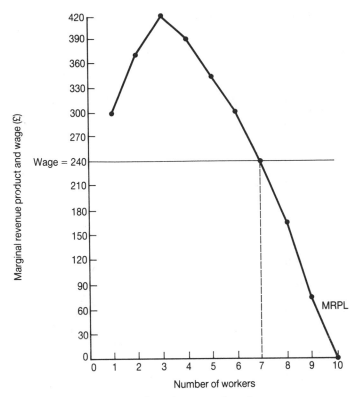

Fig. 7.1 Determination of number of workers employed

Fig. 7.2). The situation being brought about either by an increase in the productivity of the workforce or by a rise in the selling price of the good produced.

7.4 Interference in the labour market

A criticism often levelled at the application of marginal productivity theory in the labour market is that it lacks relevance in situations where trade unions and employers' organisations have the power to influence wage levels.

In the building industry, the unions are fully represented on the industry's joint negotiating bodies and attempt to maintain construction workers' earning levels. On the employers' side, there are two organisations, whose members employ over three quarters of the workers in the private sector of the industry.

Yet there is a higher turnover of labour and a lower level of unionisation than in many other industries. A high degree of mobility in construction work being inevitable given the varying nature of demand.

7.5 Economic Rent

When looking at the incomes received by the suppliers of labour and the other

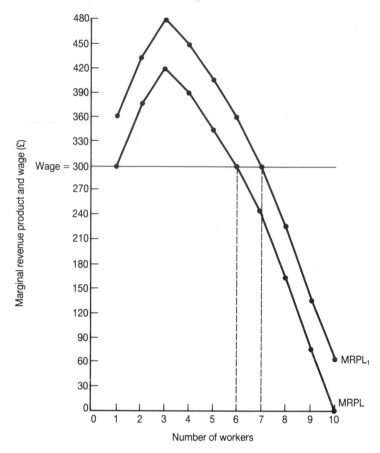

Fig. 7.2 Effects of a wage increase

factors of production, one important concept to consider is that of *economic rent*.

The term economic rent has been inherited from nineteenth century economists (notably David Ricardo) who were concerned with the problems of agricultural land. Ricardo took the view that as land is obviously immobile, a landowner would put his land to use as long as he could obtain an adequate return on the labour and capital involved.

In other words, land in general has no transfer cost (i.e. opportunity cost) and so the whole of landowners' income is a surplus in the sense that it is an income over and above that which is necessary to maintain the land in use.

Economists noticed that other factors also possess this same characteristic and so any factor's income above its transfer income may be termed an economic rent.

7.5.1 An example of pure economic rent

Few factors of production are completely fixed (or completely mobile) but in instances where the supply of land or any other factor is perfectly inelastic (i.e. the supply is fixed), then the level of demand is the sole active determinant of the owner's income. Fig. 7.3 illustrates this point.

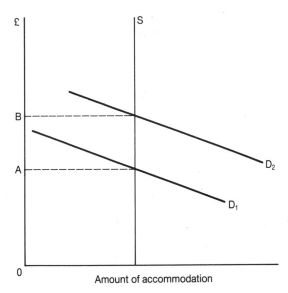

Fig. 7.3 The effect of an increase in demand for property fixed in supply

   This could depict the situation facing the owner of a property fixed in size, which is committed to say commercial use only. The income he receives therefore depends upon the demand for office accommodation. Any increase in demand (shown by a shift from D_1 to D_2) raises his income (by £AB per unit of accommodation). The property owner has not increased the amount of accommodation available but has simply reaped the benefits of a change in demand conditions.
   This type of 'unearned' surplus payment often attracts the attention of economists who take the view that such incomes are highly suitable targets for penal rates of taxation due to the fact that income could be taxed without affecting the supply of the property or land.

7.5.2 Urban land

An owner of land in the centre of a town or city may be able to obtain a high level of income from it. Since the opportunity to use it for other than building land is almost non-existent, all the income from it can be thought of as an economic rent.
   However, in any particular use, a site does have a transfer cost – the income it can earn when put to another use. For instance, some areas in a city centre may at present be used by retailers who are willing to pay higher rents than commercial users. So the land or property owner's income is only partially an economic rent.

7.5.3 General applications of economic rent

The principle of economic rent can also be applied to other factors of production even when they are not necessarily fixed in supply.

Example

We can take the example of one particular category of labour – bricklayers. Fig. 7.4 shows the market for bricklayers' services.

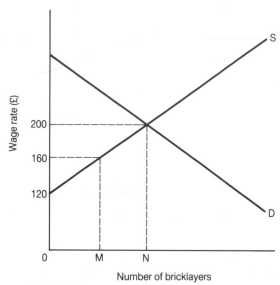

Fig. 7.4 The market for bricklayers' services

The going wage is £200 per week and the number of men employed, and all in receipt of this same wage, is ON.

The supply curve shows that there is no-one prepared to work for a wage of less than £120 pw and as the wage increases, so more and more workers are attracted to this employment.

A wage of £160 pw, for instance, is just enough to attract worker OM and £160 pw is therefore his *transfer earnings* or *opportunity cost*. He must have other employment options open to him and if he is not paid at least £160 pw he will transfer his labour elsewhere.

The difference between the actual wage he is paid and his transfer earnings can be thought of as a surplus payment or economic rent. The same applies to any of the workers employed. The wage each is paid consists partly of transfer earnings and partly of an economic rent payment. The extent of the economic rent payment varies from worker to worker – from £80 pw for the first worker to virtually £0 pw for worker ON who has to be paid £200 pw to persuade him to work.

Fig. 7.5 shows that, of the aggregate wage payments, the portion below the supply curve is made up of transfer earnings and that above it indicates the degree of economic rent.

Whilst people in ordinary occupations may be able to enjoy economic rents, those who possess a scarce talent or skill – notably in the fields of entertainment or sport – may receive incomes far in excess of the amount required to persuade them to carry out that occupation. Such surplus payments are sometimes referred to as a 'rent of talent'.

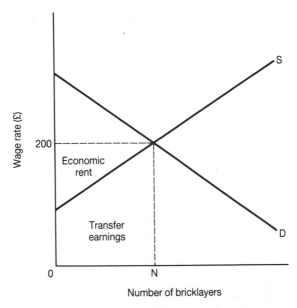

Fig. 7.5 Relationship between economic rent and transfer earnings

7.5.4 Quasi-rent

A quasi-(economic) rent is distinguished from a true economic rent because the former disappears over time. A true economic rent persists and the factor concerned must have the essential quality of uniqueness.

Most factors are immobile to some degree or other for a certain length of time, but if high returns are earned there is an increase in their supply and this eliminates the economic rent.

Quasi-rents often apply in the case of capital. For instance, a shortage of office accommodation in a town caused by a sudden increase in demand may cause commercial rents to rise but this situation is alleviated as new development takes place. In the case of labour, the length of time taken to acquire a skill or the ability of a professional body to restrict entry into an occupation often determines the extent to which economic rent can persist.

Exercises

7.1 The going wage in the industry is £210 per week and the marginal physical product per week of each additional worker employed by a firm is as given below:

Number of workers employed	1	2	3	4	5
Marginal physical product	5	7	9	7	4

If each unit sells for £30, explaining your answer, what is the firm's demand for labour?

(ISVA)

7.2 The total output per day (bricks laid), as the number of bricklayers employed by a builder is increased, is shown in the table below:

Number of workers		1	2	3	4	5	6	7
Total physical production (000)		2	5	9	12	14	15	15

What is:

a) the level of employment of bricklayers at which production is most efficient and

b) marginal physical product?

Suggest reasons for the change in marginal physical product as more bricklayers are employed.

(ISVA)

7.3 With the aid of a diagram, explain 'economic rent' and show how it arises. Examine the ways in which the concept can be applied to factors of production other than land.

7.4 What do you understand by the term 'quasi-rent'? How does it arise and how does it differ from economic rent?

7.5 A government valuer earns £1200 pm. He is offered a position in private practice as an auctioneer at £1500 pm.

If he accepts:

a) what is his opportunity cost?

b) what is his economic rent?

c) what are his transfer earnings?

d) what is his quasi-rent?

Briefly state what is likely to determine whether his economic rent will persist.

(ISVA)

7.6 C owns a plot of land which backs on to the properties of A and B. B leases C's plot at £200 per annum for use as a parking space. A who runs a greengrocery business, knowing that B's lease is about to expire, offers C £800 per annum for a building lease on the plot. C accepts.

a) What was the economic rent of the plot before A made his bid?

b) What was the economic rent of the plot after the transaction between A and C?

(ISVA)

7.7 Giving brief reasons for each answer, indicate whether the following statements with regard to the marginal revenue product curve are true or false.

a) One reason why the MRP curve slopes downward from left to right is because, as more of the commodity is produced and sold, the price will fall.

b) If there is an improvement in the productivity of the variable factor employed in producing a commodity, the MRP curve will shift downwards and to the left.

c) An increase in the costs of the variable factor at all levels of employment will result in a shift upwards and to the right of the MRP curve.

(ISVA)

8

The Size of Firms

8.1 The importance of small firms in industry

With three-quarters (in 1990) of the firms in the building industry each having less than 30 employees, there are few other sections of the economy in which small business plays such a prominent part.

In spite of this fact though, the trend in construction, as in other sectors, has been one of a decline in the importance of small firms. As long ago as 1963, the 'Bolton Committee of Inquiry on Small Firms' found 89% of construction firms with 25 or less employees.

8.2 Reasons for the existence of small firms

Small firms have a vital role to play in the economy and there are many reasons for the encouragement given by the government in recent years to the setting up of small businesses. Some of the more important of these being:

a) Small firms produce a disproportionately large number of innovations. The management of such firms are in many ways closer to the market and can be more flexible in catering for the changing needs of their customers.
b) The industry's product may have to be produced for a market which is highly dispersed or, as is specifically the case for the building industry, production may have to be site based.
c) The overall market may only be relatively small and does not warrant the development of even one large producer. This may be the case when a firm is producing a highly customised good.
d) Large firms may subcontract smaller firms to provide specific services and products for which the former do not have a large or constant demand. In construction this is common practice, but also in such industries as engineering and vehicle manufacture the large manufacturers often contract out for specialised components.

Yet it is nevertheless true that in many industries, there are certainly advantages to be gained by a firm if it grows larger and is able to develop *economies of scale*.

8.3 Economies of scale in the long-run

A firm's optimal level of production occurs when the firm is operating at its most efficient size, i.e. where its unit costs are at their lowest.

The long-run is not a specified period of time but is the time-scale required to be able to vary all the factors of production. The firm has sufficient time to be able to acquire new equipment, build new premises etc and so should be able to assess accurately the level of demand for its product and achieve the optimum level of production in this situation.

8.3.1 The long-run average cost curve

As the firm is able to extend its productive capacity by expanding its existing production plant or acquiring new ones, a series of short-run average cost curves can be envisaged representing the costs at different scales of production. Fig. 8.1 illustrates this idea.

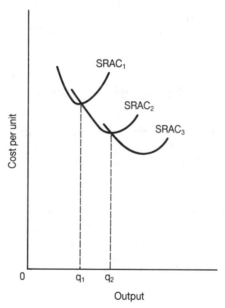

Fig. 8.1 Short-run average cost curves

$SRAC_1$ represents the unit (or average) costs associated with the firm's initial plant. According to the 'Law of Diminishing Returns' these costs can be expected (after a certain level of output is reached) to rise. This output is q_1 in the diagram. Rather than raise production in its existing plant it would be better for the firm to develop a new plant instead. Advantage can now be taken of the increasing returns to scale and thus lower unit costs associated with this second plant as shown by the curve $SRAC_2$. Further increases in output will lead to a point where the firm must consider operating a further new plant. Beyond an output level of Oq_2 unit cost curve $SRAC_3$ is shown for a third plant.

8.3.2　Why the curves move downwards

It is assumed here that the firm has an incentive for expansion in the form of lower costs. The explanation for this is that the firm can gain certain economies of scale as it moves from one level of production to the next and these economies are only possible as it increases the level of its output by moving to a larger and larger scale of production.

8.3.3　Economies of scale

These economies associated with large-scale production can arise for several different reasons, which may be categorised as follows:

a) Management and administration. The firm may be able to spread some of its managerial and administrative costs over production at a few plants. For instance, the firm may still only employ one personnel manager or one accountant even if it has two or three plants. The number of clerical staff would be unlikely to double if the firm doubled its output capacity.
b) Specialisation of equipment. Only a large-scale producer may find it feasible to use specialist machinery and methods to enhance production. The use of production line techniques and computerised systems being examples of such methods.
c) Distribution. Larger firms can make fuller use of available transport facilities. Existing vehicles may be used to full capacity and more materials and goods transported in the same time period. Also, if the capacity of wagons or containers is, say doubled, there may be no need to increase the number of personnel needed to operate the vehicles and other costs are unlikely to rise proportionately.
d) Materials. Discounts on the bulk purchase of materials reduce unit costs.
e) Finance. The larger a firm the greater the variety of sources of available finance open to it. This factor normally means that the cost of raising finance is lower.
f) Research. In any industry liable to technological change, it is the larger firms which are able to develop and take advantage of innovations in order to reduce costs. This is especially true in the use of computerised control systems.

8.3.4　The optimal size of the firm in the long-run

There will come a point for any firm when it will have reached its optimal level of long-term production, i.e. it will have achieved the scale of production at which its overall long-run average costs are at their lowest. Expansion beyond this point means that the firm begins to suffer from *diseconomies of scale*, which means that as output is increased unit costs begin to rise.

Fig. 8.2 shows that the firm's short-run average cost curves can be summed to give the long-run average cost curve. This firm is at its most efficient when it operates five plants and produces an overall output of OQ.

Once the firm goes beyond this optimum level of output, unit costs may begin to rise as diseconomies of scale develop. Fig. 8.3 shows the U-shaped long-run average cost curve which may exist for firms in many industries. Beyond the output OQ it would not pay the firm to open any more plants.

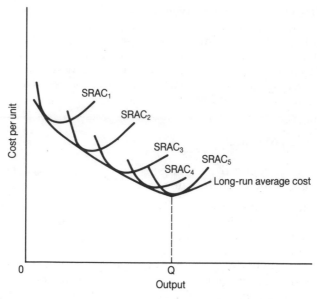

Fig. 8.2 The long-run average cost curve enveloping the short-run average cost

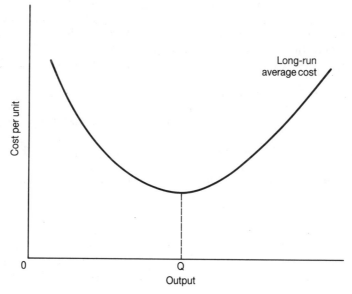

Fig. 8.3 Long-run average cost curve

8.3.5 The limits to economies of scale

By extensive specialisation and by the development of large industrial complexes, firms may be able to take advantage of technological factors that tend to promote economies of scale. Yet there are likely to be several factors that limit such economies and thus the efficient development of a firm.

Examples of this type of diseconomy are as follows:

a) Decision making channels become more and more complex as the size of the firm increases. Communications become progressively more difficult and managerial inefficiency inevitably appears.
b) Existing sources of materials may not be adequate to meet the increased demand for them and it may be difficult or expensive to develop new ones.
c) Specific labour shortages may arise especially in industries requiring a highly skilled work force with wage payments having to be raised to attract the necessary workers.
d) A firm's growth may be constrained by the market for its products. The development of new markets – resulting from diversification into new product areas or into export fields for instance – may prove to be a costly business.

8.3.6 Optimal size

The scale of production at which any of these diseconomies arise will depend upon the type of industry involved. Optimum size (i.e. least-cost production) varies from one industry to another. In certain lines of production – steel, cars and cigarettes for example – large size is particularly effective. Yet in other types of industry, such as construction, medium and small sized firms predominate.

Different sizes are obviously optimal in different types of production but the numbers of firms who actually operate at the optimal scale are probably quite few. If there is an optimum size for firms in an industry it might seem pertinent to ask why all firms are not exactly that size. There can be several explanations for this.

Firstly, a firm cannot calculate its costs precisely and there are inevitably errors in judgement. Secondly, a firm cannot always predict technological changes and may build an optimal size plant one day only to find it non-optimal the next. Lastly, a firm may have expansion as a major objective and may be willing to sacrifice some efficiency purely to obtain a large size.

8.4 Methods of growth

There are several directions in which a firm can grow in size and, as it grows, it rarely confines itself to one such direction. It is possible to distinguish between three basic types of development according to the stage and field of production into which a firm expands.

i) *Horizontal integration.* This refers to expansion by setting up or by buying up more plants to make a given product. In other words, expansion occurs at the same stage of production. For instance, one timber merchant takes over another merchant.

The purpose of such development may be to gain the economies of scale likely to arise from operating more than one timber yard. The firm may also possibly need to expand in order to withstand competition from other large firms in the industry.

ii) *Vertical integration.* A situation where one firm combines with another firm at a different stage in the productive process. This is referred to as forward vertical integration if a firm moves a stage nearer to the final customer. A timber merchant who sets up his own retail outlets would be an example. It is often the desire to cut out the middleman that prompts such action.

Backward vertical integration on the other hand occurs when a firm looks backward towards its sources of supplies and a merger occurs in order to ensure the supply of materials. A timber merchant who merged with a firm of timber importers would be an example of this.

iii) *Lateral integration.*   This arises when a firm wishes to diversify and moves into similar but slightly different product markets. This often occurs with large companies, especially in the foodstuffs and leisure industries, where consumers' tastes tend to change rapidly. In the case of our timber merchants an extension of the business to supply other building materials (such as glass or cement products) might be a natural development. Fig. 8.4 illustrates all these different growth patterns.

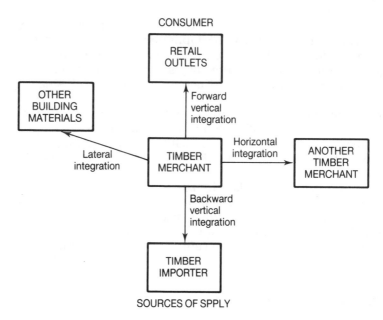

Fig. 8.4 Types of integration

8.5 Large firms

Finally, it is worth looking at which types of firms are the largest in the country. Table 8.1 shows the largest industrial companies in the U.K. when ranked by turnover.

The oil industry predominates here along with the newly privatised power industry. The other companies which figure prominently are those such as BAT and Hanson, who have successfully diversified over a period of time into different areas of production by mergers and take-overs.

Table 8.1 Largest industrial organisations

Rank	Company	Main activities
1	British Petroleum Company	Oil
2	Shell Transport & Trading	Oil
3	BAT Industries	Tobacco, retailing, paper and financial services
4	ICI	Petrochemicals, pharmaceuticals
5	Electricity Council	Electricity suppliers
6	British Telecom	Telecom services
7	British Gas	Gas suppliers
8	Hanson	Consumer products
9	Shell U.K.	Oil
10	Grand Metropolitan	Hotel and brewers

(Source: *The Times 1000*, 1990)

8.6 Multi-national corporations

The ultimate natural development in the process of growth of a company is for it to operate in more than one country – to become a multi-national.

One of the main reasons for the establishment of plants in different countries is the cost advantage that results from not having to transport goods over great distances. Once established there are other benefits, especially in high technology industries where a company can be in a position to ensure that technical developments in one country are transferred to its plants in other countries. In fact, a multi-national company is more likely than most to have the necessary financial capital available to devote to research and development.

Yet in times of economic recession, probably the greatest advantage to a company of being a multi-national is that the diversity of location provided by having units in different countries means that the company is better able to withstand any problems being experienced in one country. A multi-national might be in a far better position than a localised company to endure the set-backs resulting from industrial relations problems or temporarily declining markets.

As with any large organisation, a multi-national can suffer the normal managerial and decision-making problems associated with such bodies. This is especially true when different cultural and economic systems are involved, as they often are when companies from the rich industrialised nations extend their interest into the developing areas of the world.

The main source of controversy over the years, concerning these large corporations has been the conflict of interests that may appear to arise between the owners and management of a foreign parent company on the one hand, and the workers and public of the host country on the other. This has been an inevitable feature resulting from the international economic recession.

8.7 Growth and the development of monopolies

If one firm in an industry is able to expand and to continue to reduce its unit costs by doing so, then it is quite possible that a monopoly will develop in the industry.

Criticism is frequently made of a situation where one firm becomes dominant in an industry, on the grounds that the monopolist producer is often able to exert control over the market and charge a higher price for the product than would otherwise be the case in a competitive industry. A monopolist may, in addition, have little incentive to improve the quality of his product if he knows that his customers are unable to purchase the product elsewhere.

There are of course other ways in which monopoly power can be exerted in an industry. Producers can set up trade associations and try to divide up the market or come to 'implicit' agreements concerning price fixing. For whatever reason monopoly powers occur, governments in the U.K. have shown concern over certain industries becoming more and more concentrated, and have legislated to prevent its development.

8.8 Legal control of monopolies & mergers in the U.K.

The first Act of Parliament dealing with monopoly and restrictive practices was introduced in 1948 as the Monopolies and Trade Practices Act. The Monopolies and Mergers Commission was created under the Act and, on a reference from the Board of Trade, this Commission could investigate the supply or manufacture of products where one third or more of the market was controlled by one firm or by two or more firms with arrangements to restrict competition, i.e. restrictive practices.

One example of a restrictive arrangement investigated by the Commission in the early 1950s was the price-fixing ring operated by the London Builders Conference, which existed to agree common policy on certain matters. With the 1956 Restrictive Practices Act, restrictive agreements had to be registered and were deemed to be against the 'public interest' unless they met certain specific conditions. This Act was reinforced in 1968 when agreements simply to exchange information about prices were made subject to registration and investigation.

In the years following the 1956 Act there were significant increases in the number of mergers due to the restrictions on agreements, and the Monopolies and Mergers Commission was empowered to investigate mergers involving the acquisition of assets of £5m or more. The Board of Trade could prohibit a merger or dissolve existing monopolies.

The most comprehensive piece of legislation on 'competition policy' was the Fair Trading Act of 1973 which improved all the existing controls on monopolies, mergers and restrictive practices and set up the Office of the Director General of Fair Trading. A major role of the office being to consider whether or not a detailed inquiry should be carried out by the Commission. An important feature of the Act was that it reduced the market share criterion for a monopoly reference from a one-third share to a one-quarter share of the market and also localised monopolies were now liable to investigation. With regards to defining the 'public interest' when a monopoly was investigated, three areas of activity were specified, notably encouragement of competition, preservation of employment and the promotion of a balanced regional development.

The 1973 Act was amended by the 1980 Competition Act produced by a government concerned with placing great emphasis on the promotion of competition. A very broad definition of anti-competition practice ('has or is intended to have the effect of restricting, distorting or preventing competition') was put forward. The referral of public bodies such as nationalised industries to the Commission was one change introduced which was long overdue.

In 1988, the government reviewed its merger policy and reaffirmed its policy of leaving most merger decisions to the market.

8.8.1 The Single European Market

As a member of the European Community, the U.K. is also subject to European competition law, reflected in articles 85 and 86 of the Treaty of Rome. Agreements and practices which restrict or distort competition within the EC are prohibited. With the Single European Market, the relationship between national policy and European competition policy is an important one.

8.8.2 The effects of monopoly and merger control

Merger control policy is difficult to evaluate. For a merger to be prevented, detriment to the public interest has to be shown and it is difficult to give a satisfactory definition of this concept. There is no fully effective way of discouraging some mergers, but the mere threat of reference to the Commission has often been enough to prevent a merger. This fear of investigation has perhaps been the main weapon of the government's policy because it has at least forced companies involved in mergers to consider fully the logic of their actions.

Exercises

8.1 What reasons can you give to account for the tendency for industrial production to concentrate in a relatively few large firms?

8.2 Describe what is meant by the economies of large-scale production. State the reasons for this concept to be of limited application in the building industry.

8.3 Examine the reasons why small firms in the construction industry can exist side by side with large firms.

8.4 Explain the purpose of the government's policy to control the development of mergers and monopolies.

8.5 Distinguish between the horizontal integration and vertical integration of manufacturing firms. With the help of examples examine the factors which tend to encourage each type of integration.

9

The Location of Industry

One decision which the producer of any good or service has to make, concerns the choice of the location of his firm. There are likely to be many factors affecting such a decision, but we can identify the more important of these (including governmental interference) and analyse how they have affected the distribution of industry in the U.K.

Although chance may have a part to play in location, there are usually sound economic reasons for the development of a firm or industry in an area. Certain types of producer may be concentrated in an area for no obvious economic reason, if those factors originally responsible for setting up the industry there are no longer of consequence. Nevertheless, it is worth considering those geographical and non-geographical factors that determine industrial location, and also establish the reasons for the government's concern in the matter.

9.1 Factors affecting location decisions

a) Raw materials.   Industries requiring materials that are bulky or heavy to transport tend to be located near the source of these materials. In the case of cement manufacture, the industry developed at Rugby and along the Ribble and lower Thames valleys where the raw materials of limestone and clay are available; for brick making, local supplies of clay in the East Midlands especially around Bedford and Peterborough, provided the basic requirement.

In some cases though, the original sources of materials may have disappeared, yet an industry still carries on in an area – the steel industry in Sheffield being a case in point.

b) Markets.   There is a tendency for the producers of consumer oriented goods to ensure that they have access to their market. Many consumer durables – such as furniture – may be expensive to transport, and being close to a large population centre is the overriding factor in locational choice.

With products for which there is a significant increase in weight in the production process – such as ready-mixed concrete – proximity to the market is important. Also the manufacturers of perishable foodstuffs such as bread, are often distributing relatively small amounts to a large number of outlets and a market-based location keeps costs down.

c) Labour.   When an industry has been concentrated in an area for many years, a highly specialised and skilled workforce develops and such a location offers obvious advantages to a new firm in the industry, who may otherwise be faced with the difficulties and expense of training unskilled employees. Experienced car workers for instance, can be found predominantly in the vehicle manufacturing areas of the Midlands.

Firms are not likely to find though, that there are significant differences in labour costs between different locations, as national wage agreements have greatly eroded regional wage differentials.

d) Other industries. The existence of a main industry in an area attracts subsidiary industries to that area. Firms producing car components, upholstery firms and others providing ancillary equipment for the major car producers tend to be found in the vehicle manufacturing areas; the development of the wire industry in Warrington arose from the steel industry in South Lancashire.

More generally, once an area develops an industrial base, the development of transport facilities, such as motorway link roads and bus services for local workers and the provision of public utilities, may attract other (not necessarily 'linked') firms to that area. Industrial estates providing facilities for a diverse range of firms have become a feature of many growing towns.

e) Land. The availability of large amounts of cheap land attracts those industries which require a large area for their operations. This is the case, for example, with steel production and oil refineries.

For many manufacturers, once they have decided to set up in a particular area, the choice may have to be made between a location close to a town centre or a suburban location, i.e. the advantages of access to specialised, commercial services and easy access to a pool of labour afforded by a central location must be weighed against the normally cheaper land and lower rates in out-of-town sites.

Overall, in spite of these factors, a lot of industry in the U.K. could, to a degree, be considered footloose in the sense that the economic advantage of locating in different areas does not vary greatly. The U.K. is a relatively small country in terms of area, and substantial growth in the national motorway system in the 1970s greatly improved communication links between the regions of the country.

Many location decisions may be based on non-economic factors though. Inertia on the part of firms may lead to their not even considering a move to another area when they want to expand or open a new plant. The owners or managers of a firm, for social reasons, may not be at all interested in locating in those parts of the country considered to be undesirable ones in which to live and work.

There is one more vital factor to consider. The government, for various purposes, has attempted over the years to influence the location of industry throughout the country. The reasons behind such policy and its effects can now be looked at.

9.2 Government intervention

Left to his own devices, a producer will choose that location which is most beneficial for his firm. From the government's viewpoint, it is the overall effect of the distribution of industry throughout the country that results from the thousands of individual location decisions that is its concern.

Problems arising from a policy of 'laissez faire' with respect to the location of organisations have resulted in a policy of intervention by successive governments over past decades. This type of governmental interference comes under the heading of 'regional policy' as the government is interested in ensuring an adequate distribution of resources throughout the various regions of the U.K.

9.3 The regional problem

There has been a regional problem in this country since the 1930s and it has traditionally been a problem of an imbalance between the regions in terms of unemployment and in the availability of jobs. The problem arose from the fact that the country's basic industries of the nineteenth and early twentieth centuries (i.e. textiles, iron and steel, coal and shipbuilding) had begun to decline and these industries tended to be concentrated in certain areas. The heavy concentration of textiles in Lancashire and the strong reliance on coal and shipbuilding in the North East of England, for instance, produced highly specialised industrial areas. The depression years of the early 1930s resulted in high unemployment rates in these basic industries – over 60% in shipbuilding in 1933 – and some parts of the country consequently suffered far more than others. The problem in the post-war period might have been reduced had the new growth industries, especially vehicle production and electrical engineering, taken the place of the declining industries in the depressed areas. The weakened regions did not tend to attract the new industry and the employment balance was not restored.

9.4 The development of regional policy

Since explicit regional policy began in the U.K. in 1934, the measures that have been undertaken to solve this problem have been many and varied. The problem can be interpreted as one of an imbalance of resources between the regions of the country and viewed in this light there are two basic solutions to the problem. These are:

a) The migration of workers from regions of high unemployment to areas where there may be labour shortages or at least better prospects of employment; in other words 'workers to the work' policy.
b) The location of new industry and the relocation of footloose industry away from full employment areas to the regions of high unemployment, i.e. taking 'work to the workers'.

As the first solution would create too many social problems, most measures have been aimed at attempting to influence industrial location.

9.4.1 Inducements to industry

Over the years the strength of government action to influence the geographical distribution of industry has fluctuated considerably according to the changing fortunes of the national economy. Throughout the 1960s and early 1970s successive governments introduced new measures and a major criticism was made by industry of the speed with which policy was changed.

Generally though, the mainstay of regional policy has been the use of grants and loans given for capital expenditure on building and machinery undertaken by manufacturing firms in the worse-off areas, even though the designation of the areas and the rates of grant have often changed. The obvious assumption behind such grants being that the expansion of industry must lead to the creation of more jobs in these areas.

A criticism of this principle may be made on the grounds that money spent on subsidies to firms for hiring labour would be a more direct method of creating jobs, and even though this had been tried (notably with the Regional Employment Premium in the 1960s and 1970s) capital subsidies have not tended to be matched by similar assistance to labour.

Other inducements have included the payment of removal costs and other relocation expenses for firms moving to the worse-off areas. Also, the government has provided purpose built industrial accommodation at low cost as part of its advance factory programme. One notable example of this was the attempt by the government to develop a motor manufacturing industry in Scotland by persuading Rootes (later Peugeot) to move to a new plant at Linwood.

A policy complementary to one of inducements, concerns the restriction of industrial growth in the richer areas of the country in the hope that firms will be 'pushed' into the desired regions. To check the expansion of industrial sites, particularly in London and the South East, Industrial Development Certificates (IDCs) had been used since 1948. To build or extend premises beyond certain limits, an IDC was required in some areas of the country but not in the worse-off regions.

9.4.2 Regional policy 1972 to 1984

The Industry Act of 1972 introduced a detailed scheme of regional assistance.

The system was based on the identification of 'Assisted Areas' selected as those parts of the country with the worst economic problems. Three types of area in need of assistance were designated – Special Development Areas with the highest unemployment rates, Development Areas and Intermediate Areas. The type and level of assistance available in a particular area being based on the area's status.

The main form of assistance consisted of the Regional Development Grant (RDG). As a grant towards capital investment in building, plant or machinery for manufacturing purposes in the Assisted Areas it provided an incentive for industrial development. The rate of grant depended on the grade of Assisted Area with the maximum grant being 22%.

Further assistance was also available in the Assisted Areas for undertakings which maintained employment. Projects in the construction industry were also eligible for this aid.

9.4.3 Regional policy since 1984

A new U.K. regional policy was introduced in 1984 which put more emphasis on actual job creation rather than on investment. It was estimated that between 1972 and 1983 the previous regional policy created some 500 000 jobs, but it was felt that the 1970s regional policy was not sufficiently selective, discriminated against services, favoured capital-intensive projects and most importantly was not cost-effective.

Under the policy introduced in 1984 there were two types of region – Development areas and Intermediate areas (see Fig. 9.1). Firms in Development areas qualifying for both RDGs, determined by eligible capital expenditure or job creation, and regional selective assistance (RSA). It was announced in 1988 that the RDG scheme was to be phased out, leaving the discretionary

RSA (mainly based on project and training grants) as the main source of regional industrial assistance available in both areas.

In addition, U.K. government support is available for inner cities and enterprise zones which were established to be complementary to regional policy with the purpose of improving economic life in inner city, unemployment blackspots.

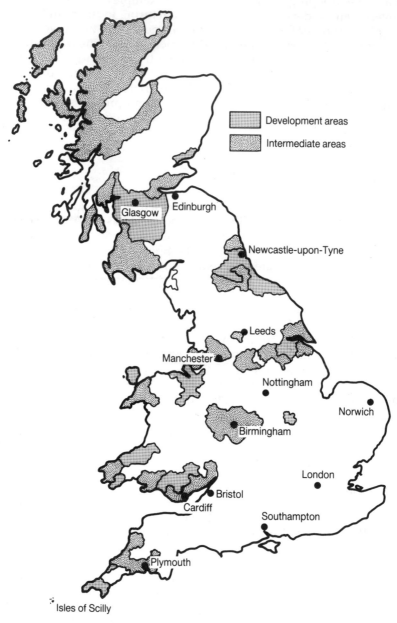

Fig. 9.1 Great Britain Assisted Areas

9.4.4 Regional aid and the European Community

The regional aid provided by the U.K. government is complemented by financial assistance from the European Community. This aid is mainly directed at 'less developed' regions and in the U.K. this means areas of industrial decline (most of the U.K. from the Midlands northwards) and declining rural areas.

The funds used to be allocated to each country on a quota basis but now assistance is only available for projects approved by the European Commission. The interpretation of this assistance taken by the U.K. government is that EC assistance is used to match U.K. funding and thereby reduces the state's own commitment. But this conflicts with the EC's view that the U.K. government should honour its own original commitment.

9.4.5 An appraisal of regional policy

It is obviously contentious to determine the effects of regional policy on the employment structure and pattern of industrial location in the U.K. However, the fact that wide unemployment rate differentials between the regions still exist in the 1990s (Table 9.1) does indicate a degree of failure to remedy the fundamental problem.

Table 9.1 Regional unemployment rates

Region	Unemployment rate (%) June 1991
North	10.3
North West	9.5
South East	6.9
East Anglia	5.8

(Source: Department of Employment)

Exercises

9.1 Give reasons for the generally dispersed location of the construction industry in the U.K.
9.2 Why do some firms establish new factories in areas other than the less prosperous regions, even though the Government may offer financial inducements to those who locate in the latter?
9.3 a) What reasons have led to the location of industries in various areas?
   b) Discuss the extent to which these reasons apply to the construction industry.

10

Business Organisations and the Raising of Finance

The nature of the work undertaken by the construction industry means that it must inevitably consist of organisations of many different sizes. The form of organisation of a firm varies according to the functions of the business. The great majority of companies are owned and run by one or two people yet the limited company, owned by shareholders is predominant in British industry and business.

The various forms of business organisation and the economic implications of their structure are described in the following section

10.1 Forms of business

10.1.1 The sole trader

This is the simplest form of business organisation and whilst it may not necessarily be a 'one-man' business, a single person provides the capital and takes the risks involved in running the business.

It is a type of organisation particularly prevalent in the building industry. Yet as the sole trader legally has unlimited liability he is personally liable for all the debts of the business, up to the limits of his whole estate. So in an industry where capital needs to be tied up in equipment and cash flow problems easily arise, it is not surprising that such a high bankruptcy rate exists.

Sole traders often play a prominent role in industries providing a personal service, such as retailing or building services, and are often able to survive in the face of competition from larger rivals due to their ability to build up good personal relationships with customers. The biggest drawback for this form of business tends to be lack of finance due to its dependence on the commercial banking system and its inability to obtain the same sort of credit facilities as larger organisations.

10.1.2 The partnership

A partnership exists when two or more people combine together in business with a view to profit. Partnerships may not normally consist of more than twenty partners with the exception of partnerships of certain professions. It is a particularly suitable form of organisation for professions such as estate agents, surveyors or architects.

A partnership arrangement holds several advantages over a sole trader, notably an ability to pool capital resources and the fact that its often flexible structure allows for specialisation amongst partners.

Any partner is, however, subject to unlimited liability in the same manner as a sole trader, unless he is a 'sleeping' partner in which case he pays for his liability protection by not being allowed to take part in the running of the business.

10.1.3 The private limited company

For a business to operate on a large scale it is normally necessary for it to become a limited company. This represents a way in which large numbers of people can contribute funds to an organisation without the risk of losing their personal estate.

The private limited (or joint stock) company consists of an association of at least two people who hold shares (the joint stock) in the company. A limited company often arises as a result of the expansion of a partnership and commonly from a family business.

Each shareholder is entitled to a share in the company's profits, but if the company makes losses, each shareholder is limited in his liability to the amount he paid for the shares. The fact that the company has a legal personality separate from that of the shareholders gives them this privilege of limited liability.

One drawback for a business which may consider becoming a limited company is that the affairs of a company are closely controlled by various Companies Acts, and it must trade within the objects as set out in its registration. Also, the affairs of the company are more public than those of the partnership as it is required to file its accounts with the Registrar of Companies.

10.1.4 The public limited company (plc)

This is basically an extension of the private company. 'Plc's are generally the giants of the business world.

The shares of a public company may be offered for public subscription and they may be offered for resale without restriction. This means that this form of company is virtually essential for large-scale business where large amounts of capital are required.

In many public companies there must inevitably be less involvement by shareholders in the company management. The directors of the company may be elected by shareholders, but outside annual general meetings the owners of the company may have little chance of directly influencing company policy.

Investment in public companies can be attractive to an investor who wishes to spread his funds and is not particularly interested in direct participation in those companies.

A major problem for many organisations – particularly in the construction industry – involves obtaining finance. Public companies are able to attract funds from a wide variety of sources including the financial institutions and institutional investors, due to the ease with which shares can be transferred.

The availability (or non-availability) of capital from different sources constitutes an important factor in the ability of an organisation to develop. Consequently it is worth considering the various ways in which these differing types of business obtain their finance.

10.2 Sources of capital

Any organisation beginning operations normally has to find the initial financial capital from the owners or friends and relations as no one else may be willing to take the risk of lending capital to an unknown enterprise.

As the firm eventually prospers though, the profits made can be ploughed back into the enterprise. The more profitable the enterprise the greater its ability to be self-financing as its business generates more funds for the continuance of trade. Such a business is also likely to be more attractive to the institutions who might be willing to lend money to the firm.

10.2.1 External finance

Any firm's ability to generate internal finance is limited and to develop it must usually turn to external sources and the financial capital markets.

The way in which a business can raise finance from external sources depends to a large degree on the size and type of firm – only limited companies, for instance, being able to raise share capital.

The main sources of external finance for a business are shown in Fig. 10.1.

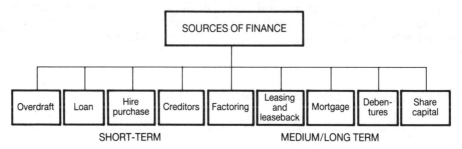

Fig. 10.1 Sources of finance

Short-term finance
Overdrafts
Bank overdrafts are a most important source of short-term finance. To overcome immediate cash flow problems that may arise when materials have to be purchased or payments made to subcontractors, businesses need to borrow on a temporary basis.

For many building firms the ability to obtain materials on credit from builders' merchants represents a vital source of immediate finance.

Term loans
A short-term loan may be an alternative to an overdraft, with the credit standing of a business determining its ability to obtain the loan and also the rate of interest charged.

For medium-term loans of larger sums, security such as a piece of property or land normally has to be offered against the loan.

Other short-term finance
Hire-purchase represents an important source of finance enabling small businesses in particular to purchase machinery and equipment.

Holding back payment to creditors until the last possible stage is a particularly prevalent practice in the building industry as in many other industries and this procedure tends to reduce the need to call upon other short-term finance facilities such as overdrafts.

One function of finance houses is to purchase the outstanding debts of companies; a process which is termed factoring. The company does of course have to pay for this service but it does mean that the company does not have its money tied up in debtors.

For many construction jobs, the system of interim payments by customers to cover costs incurred along the way means that firms often do not need to have large amounts of capital tied up.

Long-term finance
Leasing and leaseback
An alternative to the outright purchase of equipment and machinery (particularly vehicles) is leasing. This enables the firm to have more capital available for the business.

For the same reason a company may choose to dispose of the most substantial assets – its properties – in order to realise money which it can put to useful purpose. Under a *sale and leaseback* arrangement a company sells some of its premises and leases them back from the purchaser. In this way its fixed assets can be converted to working capital.

Mortgages
As the purchase of property is normally the largest investment a business undertakes, long-term mortgage finance is required. Companies obtain loans from the commercial banks and building societies in the same way as do individuals.

Debentures
These are simply loans made to a company which usually carry a fixed rate of interest and are repayable at set dates.

A debenture holder is not a member of the company but is normally entitled to interest on his debentures whether a company earns profits or not. The issuing of debentures does give a degree of flexibility in the raising of capital.

It is important though, that an issue of debentures is made at the right time. In a period of high interest rates, a company may undertake a commitment which appears unduly costly when interest rates fall at a future point.

Share capital
In one sense, *ordinary share capital* might be considered a cheap form of finance for a company because no cost is involved. The shareholders do not receive a fixed rate of interest on their investment but receive a share of the profits once all other claims have been met. However, if satisfactory payments are not made to shareholders they will lose confidence in the company.

Of the various categories of shareholders that exist in limited companies, it is the holders of ordinary shares who bear the greatest risk because if a business is not operating profitably they may receive no payment at all.

Preference shareholders, as the name suggests, take priority over ordinary shareholders when it comes to payments and they receive a fixed rate of interest on their holdings. Cumulative preference shares represent an even more secure investment because the dividend payment can be carried forward to future years if payments are not made for some periods.

As explained in an earlier section, a private company is not usually allowed the facility to raise large amounts of capital because it must rely on the fact that persons knowing of its existence are willing to subscribe.

10.3 Government assistance for small businesses

In spite of the fact that small businesses play such a prominent role in the construction industry, the number of small firms in the whole economy set against population is relatively few when the U.K. is compared to other EC countries.

As part of the government's desire to encourage investment through the development of small businesses, new sources of venture capital have arisen. Most important is the Business Expansion Scheme by which individuals can enjoy tax relief on limited share capital held for a number of years. To encourage financial institutions to provide medium-term loans, the government's Loan Guarantee Scheme has given incentives to the clearing banks to make loans (backed by a government guarantee on 80% of the value) available to small businesses. Also, the Enterprise Allowance Scheme has assisted the setting up of new businesses by providing a working capital allowance for an initial period in which a new venture might often experience financial difficulties.

Exercises

10.1 Distinguish between the main forms of business enterprise, noting the main economic advantages of each.

10.2 Outline the main forms of business organisation within the construction industry. Explain the reasons for the existence of the large number of small firms.

10.3 Describe the sources of finance available to a construction firm and indicate briefly the circumstances in which the use of each source would be most appropriate.

Part Four

The Building and Property Industries

11

The Structure of the Building Industry

11.1 The construction industry and the economy

The construction industry plays a central role in Britain's economy. The industry's net output amounts to some 7% of national output, and related industries, such as building materials and plant, add a further 5%. Construction contributes just under a half of the nation's fixed investment and the industry is making an increasing contribution to exports. It is also a major source of employment, with almost two million people being employed in construction and directly related activities. The economic significance of the construction industry means that it must play a key part in the achievement of any national government's social objectives – whether in the field of housing, health or education – and must also have an important role in industrial strategy as the regeneration of industry cannot be achieved without the modernisation and replacement of industrial buildings and infrastructure.

The public sector indeed plays an important role in creating demand for the industry's products. This reliance on the public sector means that expenditure policies as they affect both central and local government have significant effects on the level of construction work.

On the supply side, whilst many private contractors rely heavily on the public sector for their work, it is also worth considering this part of the industry separately from local authority direct labour departments who rely totally on public work.

11.2 The structure of the industry

The industry is a highly fragmented one comprised of a large number of predominantly small firms. This is not a situation which is unique to the U.K. and it reflects a rational response to the ways in which the demand for the industry's output is put. The demand for construction work is geographically dispersed and the product, by its nature, is not generally transportable. The work is highly diversified and the firms tend to specialise by type of work (only 34% of building firms in the U.K. in 1990 were classed as general builders).

The size distribution of firms and their relative importance in producing output in the private sector are shown in Table 11.1.

Table 11.1 Employment by size of firm in Great Britain 1988

Size of firm (No. employed)	Employment (%)
0–1	8.1
2–7	25.5
8–24	15.8
25–79	14.7
80–299	13.1
300–599	6.3
600 & over	16.5

(Source: Housing & Construction Statistics)

The size of firms in terms of average number of employees is low (just over 10 in 1988) and over three quarters of firms in this year employed less than eight persons. However, at the other extreme, less than one half of a per cent of all the firms in the industry employed three hundred or more persons, yet the importance of these firms in the industry is shown by the fact that they were responsible for almost a quarter of the employment and more than a third of the output.

The way in which demand is put to the industry via the contracting system allows a situation to exist where some firms are able and prepared to undertake large contracts anywhere in the country. Such contracts are relatively few though and small localised contracts predominate. Even the larger contracts tend to be sub-divided amongst specialist sub-contractors.

11.2.1 Conditions of entry into the industry

Many of the factors which normally make it advantageous for a firm in manufacturing to develop into a larger scale organisation are not present in construction. The site-based nature of production, together with the lack of standardisation of output does not lend itself to the existence of scale economies. The cost advantages of the existing firms in the industry do not therefore tend to act as a barrier to entry.

The industry also has an inherent low capital base. Most activities are essentially labour intensive and there is limited scope for the employment of fixed capital. The factory buildings of manufacturers are not needed by construction firms; many skills (such as simply laying bricks) are not easily amenable to mechanisation, and there is a well developed hire sector which services the industry and means that many specialist firms need to own little plant and equipment themselves. Working capital requirements are also limited, for although construction projects may be large, the method of interim progress payments reduces the period over which labour and materials need to be financed. The relatively low capital requirements and the comparatively high ratio of liquid to fixed capital tend to result in the industry being easy to enter.

The chances of firms gaining competitive advantage by means of controls over supplies of materials are also small. Materials constitute a major part of total costs but are drawn from a wide range of sources and no one material predominates. Backward vertical integration into the building materials industries is of little importance.

Overall, no real natural barriers to entry exist and indeed the obverse of ease of entry, a comparatively high wastage rate – between 1980 and 1986 the industry lost nearly 16% of the firms operating at the peak – tends to occur in the industry.

A decline in the private sector demand for construction is of course a reflection of a wider economic recession. But the construction industry's peculiar dependence for work in the public sector – about a half of its output being for public clients – has made it particularly vulnerable to cuts in public expenditure. This is shown by the fact that public expenditure on construction fell by about 20% between 1982–83 and 1988–89.

It is not surprising then that the part played by a major category of supplier in the public sector – direct labour organisations – should have come under much discussion in recent years.

11.3 The role of direct labour organisations (DLOs)

Direct labour has its origins in the 1890s, when local government was emerging in the form we know it today. Unemployment was high during the depression years at the end of the last century and local authority direct labour was seen by many as an effective way of creating employment. The first Works Department was set up by the London County Council in 1892 mainly to break up the monopolistic position of contractors and this lead was soon followed by several London boroughs.

The number of DLOs increased greatly after both the World Wars mainly due to the growth of council house building and, in spite of the fact that the government imposed, in 1959, a requirement that DLOs should compete for one third of their contracts and also in spite of the advent of industrialised systems of building, this growth continued in the 1960s.

During the property boom years of the early 1970s, contractors were less interested in local authority work and this meant that tender prices for council work were high. Since the collapse of the speculative building boom in 1973–74 and the decline of systems building, however, work which has normally been undertaken by DLOs has been seen by many private contractors as a reliable source of work. This growth in competition for local authority work has led to the production of several reports on DLOs in the last few years and also to changes in the law concerning their operations.

11.3.1 The justification for local authority involvement

There may be considered to be perhaps three grounds on which a case for a local authority role in the building industry could be supported.

Firstly, a merit good may be involved. This means that a good cannot be supplied privately to a wide enough section of society and in this sense the market may be said to be inefficient. This is the case for local authority housing.

Secondly, externalities arising from building may be involved. This is a matter which may be taken care of by local authority planning controls and stringent building regulations.

It is the third one which it is perhaps most important to consider here. Because public building work, especially large-scale house repair and maintenance, is such an essential service, it is vital that the supply of such a service is always readily available.

The manner in which most local authorities operate a system dealing with house repairs is that a surveyor responsible for an area or an estate takes notification of any job that needs to be done and allocates the job to the appropriate section of the direct works department as an 'initial order for work'. The job is then dealt with and the housing department charged according to the man-hours spent on the job and the materials used.

In many local authorities, especially the larger ones, any disputes over charges are resolved at monthly meetings between the managers of the direct works department and their opposite numbers in the housing and other affected departments.

The alternative is for a local authority to negotiate with contractors for, say, a yearly lump sum contract for all the maintenance work on its property. The problem with this method of dealing with repair work as far as the client local authority is concerned, is that a contractor's tender is bound to include a cost element to cover the risk of expensive, unforeseen work being required. The problems of specifying the extent to which repair work is carried out in a fast and efficient manner can also lead to a great deal of dispute.

11.3.2 Competition for local authority building work

As a result of the Local Government, Planning and Land Act of 1980, and further restrictions on their operations, local authorities have been forced by the early 1990s to open virtually all of their construction work to competition.

Faced with this competition, and with a shrinking workload due to council house sales and general cutbacks in local authority capital expenditure, it is not surprising that the value of DLO work fell every year in the decade up to 1990. The Secretary of State has the power to shut down all of, or part of, an 'unprofitable' DLO and several have been forced to move out of new-build work altogether.

Exercises

11.1 Explain why the structure of the construction industry should differ from that of manufacturing industries.

11.2 Consider the arguments for and against the existence of local authorities' own direct works departments.

11.3 'The construction industry is made up of a number of different types of market'. Discuss.

12

The Housing Market

Of the various markets that are served by the building industry, the construction and maintenance of houses is the most important in terms of value of output – in 1990, 34% of the industry's output consisted of housing work.

From an economic viewpoint, the market for housing is an interesting one to consider. There are three fairly distinct sub-markets into which the overall market can be conveniently divided, and these are distinguished according to type of ownership or tenure as follows:
1. Owner-occupation.
2. Local authority and public sector housing.
3. Privately rented and housing association accommodation.

The relative importance of these three sectors has changed over the years (See Table 12.1) – the growth of owner-occupation and the demise of the private rented sector being the major trends – and a major influence bringing about such changes has been government policy.

Table 12.1 Stock of dwellings in U.K. at end of 1990

	Housing Stock (millions) 1990 (1979)	% of total
Owner-occupation	15.4 (11.6)	67 (55)
Rented from local authorities or new town corporations	5.4 (6.8)	23 (32)
Rented from housing associations, private owners and tied accommodation	2.3 (2.9)	10 (13)
Total	23.1 (21.3)	
(Source: Social Trends)		

The provision of a satisfactory supply of housing is of great concern to any government which has a vital role to play in determining the level of supply and demand in both the public and the private sectors. Before dealing with the sectors separately it is worth considering the overall factors which affect the demand for housing.

12.1 Determinants of demand

In the long-term, the two most important influences on the general demand for housing are the size of population growth and the degree of growth in the economy. The greater the number of people, the greater the demand for housing and the more income they have, the more they will demand bigger and better houses.

A more detailed breakdown of factors is given below.

a) Household formation.   The demand for housing rises with increases in the creation of households. This demand arises mainly from new marriages and also from their breakdown when households are split up. The size of households varies over the life of a family as young people leave home and older people perhaps move in with families. Also, with migration and immigration, as households move home to find employment in other areas, localised markets will be affected.

b) Family income.   Both current income, and also the amount of income a family can expect to have in the future, determine the amount of income a family spends on housing. As incomes increase it is generally the case that people are able to make their preferences for owner-occupied property felt. This was certainly one important cause of the relative growth in owner-occupation in the 1980s shown in Table 12.1.

c) Prices.   It is a basic fact that people have to have somewhere to live and housing may be considered a necessity good. If housing costs are high though, marriages may be delayed, young people may not leave home etc, and demand will be reduced. Rising house prices may cause more families to look towards smaller property for purchase, or for rented accommodation if rent levels are kept low, and indeed for anyone in the housing market the costs of any of the various forms of accommodation must be compared.

In times of inflation in the housing market – as in the mid 1980s when house prices were rising at a faster rate than prices in general – there may be a counter effect though, where families try to purchase as large a house as they can now in the expectation of future price increases.

d) The cost and availability of finance.   In order to purchase a house most households have to take a loan from a building society or some other financial institution, and the willingness of the institution to make the finance available and the interest rate charged, determine the ability of households to make their demand effective. The importance of building society policy in making mortgage finance available was illustrated by the massive rises in house prices that went along with the increases in mortgage lending in the mid-1980s.

e) Other factors,   such as the distribution of income and preferences for owner-occupation vis-à-vis renting, also have a contributory effect on demand.

Government intervention – via rent controls, subsidies etc – is a major factor determining demand, as will become apparent when the different sectors of the market are considered in more detail.

12.2 The market for owner-occupied property

Over a period of time there has been a marked increase in the preference for home ownership, especially amongst young households. The fact that people who borrow money to buy houses for their own occupation are able effectively to obtain subsidised loans (up to a certain size), and also that house purchase involves the acquisition of a long-term inflation proof asset, have both been positive influences. The declining stock of rented accommodation and reductions in public-sector house building have also pushed households towards owner-occupation.

12.3 Finance for house purchase

An important feature of the market is the part played by building societies in making the necessary finance available for prospective house purchasers. Table 12.2 shows the dominant role of the building societies in mortgage provision.

Table 12.2 Shares of net advances for houses (%)

Year	Building Societies	Miscellaneous financial insitutions (including local authorities)	Insurance Companies	Banks
1975	75.8	20.6	1.9	1.6
1980	78.8	9.7	3.5	8.0
1981	65.8	6.3	2.5	25.4
1990	73.4	6.5	0.1	20.0

(Source: H.M.S.O. Financial Statistics)

The share of building societies in this market has been fairly consistent at about the 70% to 80% mark over the period, but the significance of the three other parties shown in the table, has varied considerably.

The insurance companies have become steadily less important, as they have tended to look elsewhere for a better return on their investments. Local authority lending reached its peak in 1974–6 when councils responded to a need to finance the purchase of mainly older properties, which the building societies were reluctant to undertake. However, cutbacks in public expenditure in the 1980s forced local authorities to move out of the market. The banks have made an effort to move into the market and offer strong competition to the building societies. Whether or not this situation persists in the future may depend upon future governments' monetary policy.

12.3.1 The origins and functions of building societies

Building societies have existed in this country for over two hundred years and originated as small groups who bought land and built houses for their members. They operated as 'terminating' societies, who were closed down once their objective had been realised and all their members housed.

In the nineteenth century, some societies began to accept investments from people who did not wish to purchase houses, and paid interest to the investors. The first 'permanent' society accepting investments and making loans for house purchase arose in the middle of that century. Development of the societies depended upon the number of houses being built for sale and considerable growth occurred during the inter-war years. This continued in the post-war period with the encouragement of owner-occupation by government and with the two private house-building booms. Nowadays, they are the only organisations whose primary concern is the finance of house purchase.

They are non-profit making organisations and any surpluses they may make are added to their reserves. Most of them belong to the Building Societies Association which negotiates with the government on the settling of interest rates and other policy matters.

The trend of building society activity throughout this century has generally been one of growth, but this expansion has been accompanied by a reduction in the number of building societies as mergers have taken place. Table 12.3 shows the decline in numbers over the years.

Table 12.3 The progress of building societies

Year	Number of societies
1900	2286
1930	1026
1960	726
1970	481
1981	251
1989	125

(Source: Housing Finance)

The Building Societies Act 1986 and the review of building society powers completed in June 1988 resulted in their being able to offer a wide range of banking and housing related services e.g. involvement in estate agency by some of the larger societies.

To achieve further involvement in banking services, the Abbey National even attained 'plc' status in 1989.

12.4 Local authority and public sector housing

The provision of housing by local authorities has been of importance since the immediate post-First World War period when the nation was faced with a shortage of houses, and the government of the day committed itself to providing 'houses for heroes'. Since that time, local authorities have been subsidised to varying degrees by central government in the building of council houses. In addition to fixing the amount of housing subsidy, central government is also able to constrain the amount of borrowing undertaken by local authorities, and thereby exert control over the building of council houses.

12.4.1 Council house rents

The general policy in public sector housing has been, for over half a century, to keep rents low, i.e. 'fair' rents and 'reasonable' rents. Basically, it is the house rather than the tenant which has been subsidised, which has led to criticisms of injustice between tenants of different financial circumstances. Rents have been based on the historic costs of providing houses rather than replacement costs not even covering the running costs involved. This means that council housing has been heavily subsidised reaching a peak of over £2.5 billion in 1981–82.

12.4.2 Council house sales

Under the 1980 Housing Act, the Conservative government introduced a provision whereby any sitting tenant who wanted to buy, had a statutory right to purchase his home and also to obtain a local authority mortgage to finance the purchase. The Conservative government actively promoted sales and, during the four year period up to 1984, over one million local authority dwellings were sold.

The sale of council houses is a contentious issue though. The previous Labour government took the view that there was no reason to object to the sale of council houses, where improving local circumstances were such that sales on reasonable terms would not impair the quality of the existing housing stock or the ability of the authority to offer accommodation to rent to those in housing need, but it should not reduce the provision of rented housing where there was an unmet demand.

The principal argument for council house sales is that people prefer to own their own houses, so they should not be denied the opportunity to do so. Also, the system ought to achieve a better distribution of housing according to need, than the situation existing with council housing, where people often tend to stay on in accommodation perhaps too big for their needs. In the short-term at least, there is no loss to the housing stock because the same people would occupy the same property anyway. A system of discounts on the market value for those purchasers who have been in tenancy for some years, may be justified on the grounds that the market price reflects the true rent earning ability of the property, whereas the local authorities may charge subsidised rents below market level anyway.

However, from the local authority's viewpoint, the sale of a house means a reduction in its stock and the replacement cost, even with government subsidies, is usually far higher than the sale price. Another major criticism, is that there is no reason why council tenants should have the privilege of cut-price ownership, when this is not offered to private house buyers.

12.5 Housing associations

The other major form of housing agency operating in the public sector is the housing association. Since the 1974 Housing Act, the housing associations have been given the status of quasi-statutory bodies in the public sector, and their expenditure is considered as part of the total housing expenditure by the government. They are mainly financed by the Housing Corporation which was set up to make loans to cost rent and co-ownership associations. Housing associations have their roots in the last century and nowadays there are over two thousand of them. Although they account for only a very small proportion of the housing stock, they often meet a need for rented accommodation not met by the private sector or by local authorities, such as special purpose housing or one person housing units. They are also able to offer different types of tenure schemes such as co-ownership and co-operatives. Such schemes can often perform the function of providing accommodation for young people who are unable to obtain a mortgage but nevertheless wish to 'invest' some of their money in a property.

12.6 Private rented sector

The decline of the private rented sector over the years has been a major feature of the housing market in the U.K. Rent control was first introduced during the

First World War as a temporary measure but has been in existence in varying degrees ever since.

The effects of this policy of keeping rents below the equilibrium level are shown in Fig. 12.1.

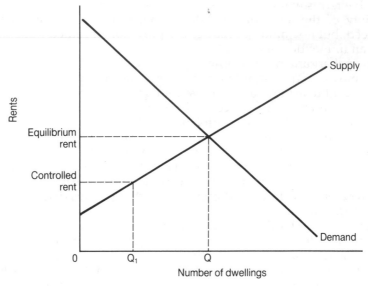

Fig. 12.1 Rent control of private rented housing

The supply of private rented accommodation has been reduced over the years (from OQ to OQ$_1$) as the low rate of return for the landlord has discouraged new building and persuaded many property owners to turn their property over to owner-occupation. Also, tax disadvantages to landlords, and rising incomes, would have led to a decline in the number of rented properties anyway. Overall though, those households who might have found rented accommodation in the private sector have had to look towards the public sector instead.

There are many people (such as students and others working away from home) who need short-term rented accommodation, and there were provisions for shorthold tenancies in the 1980 Housing Act. Uncertainty concerning the attitudes of future governments towards such tenancies and towards the private rented sector in general, probably means that the continuing decline is inevitable.

Exercises

12.1 Consider the effects on house prices of removing income tax relief on mortgage interest payments.

12.2 Examine the likely economic effects of making rent allowances to needy tenants of furnished accommodation.

(ISVA)

13

Investment and the Property Market

13.1 Property as an investment

Whilst property may be purchased solely for the purpose of occupation – a family must have a place to live, a producer needs a factory in which to manufacture his products – property can also be used as an asset for investment purposes.

Basically an investment involves the expenditure of a capital sum for which returns will occur over a period of time. On this basis, the purchase of a property can represent an investment. A sum of money is given up by the purchaser in the hope that the income he receives gives an adequate return on the outlay involved.

13.1.1 Who invests in property?

Private persons. Individuals who purchase a property, be it a house, a shop or a farm, are undertaking an investment. They make a decision to employ their financial capital for the purchase as opposed to renting a property, and the income or the satisfaction they receive from the use of the property represents the return on the investment.

Property companies. Direct investment by individuals is mainly limited to the types of property mentioned in the previous paragraph, and most investment in property is undertaken by the institutions with the large amounts of funds available, notably the insurance companies and the pension funds.

Since the first post-war property boom of 1947–59, these institutional investors have started to become much more interested in acquiring interests in commercial and modern industrial property.

In the 1960s and 70s the insurance companies became aware of the dangers of lending money to property owners and developers on fixed interest mortgages, and the advantages in participating in property ownership were apparent in a situation where rents were increasing at a faster rate than general inflation.

They increased the amount of money allocated to property investment and were joined by the pension funds and by specially formed property unit trusts and property bonds.

In the 1980s the institutions showed preference for owning their own properties. The larger institutions have also been involved in undertaking property development with their own development companies.

13.2 Development finance
13.2.1 Private sector

Apart from that building development which is carried out by private occupiers (householders and firms) for their own use, most development is carried
out by construction firms or property companies.

Residential development
With a housing development it is only the short-term finance which the
developer has to meet. (The buyer borrows in the long-term by taking out a
mortgage.) Small builders tend to have to rely on bank overdrafts, short-term
loans and suppliers' credit. Larger housebuilding firms are likely to arrange
development finance on a mixture of overdraft and medium-term loans, raised
against the overall security.

  Not all the money needs to be borrowed at once though (see Fig. 13.1) and
the builder can borrow as he requires the money throughout the period of the
development.

Commercial and industrial development
A developer who undertakes the construction of a development purely to sell it
once completed, usually obtains his finance for the development period, to
cover site acquisition and construction costs, from a commercial bank.

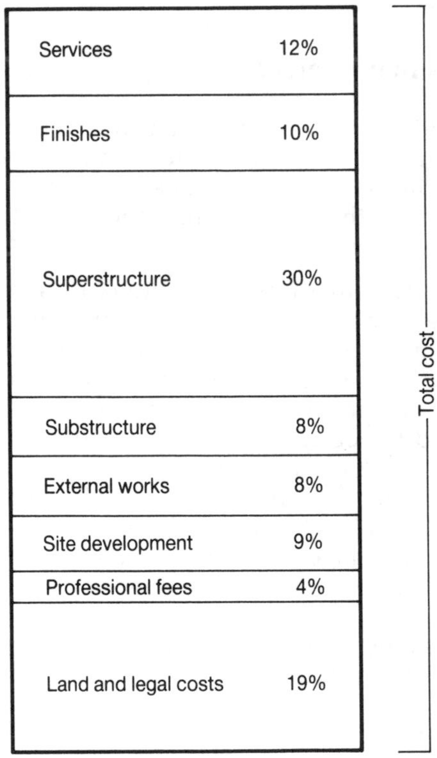

Services	12%
Finishes	10%
Superstructure	30%
Substructure	8%
External works	8%
Site development	9%
Professional fees	4%
Land and legal costs	19%

Total cost

Fig. 13.1 Housebuilding: Total cost breakdown of a typical semi-detached house

Long-term investment in property though, is the objective of property development companies who retain a property once development is completed.

As already mentioned, the existence of a development industry in this country is a relatively recent phenomenon. Commercial buildings are especially valuable financial assets and are held and traded by those institutions with funds for investment. Some commercial and industrial firms develop and redevelop their own properties but it is mainly the financial institutions who directly or indirectly provide the capital for development. The most important source of finance is the banking system, usually through subsidiaries. Yet the institutions with the most funds to invest in property are the very large pension funds, who invest in a wide variety of properties.

13.2.2 Partnership schemes

In 1981, local authority expenditure on development projects was curtailed under the 1980 Local Government, Planning and Land Act; the move tending to encourage local authorities to enter into partnership schemes with private developers. This type of scheme generally involves the local authority providing the land, with the private developer financing the development – the profits from the sale of the completed development being shared between the two parties.

13.3 Investment appraisal

A crucial decision for any potential investor to make, is whether or not a particular investment is worth undertaking, or if he is faced with a set of alternative projects, which one represents the best proposition.

A manufacturer, for instance, may have to decide on the value to the firm of an extension to his factory; a property developer must decide on the optimal size commercial development to undertake, given the state of the market for office accommodation. In situations such as these, it is necessary to use a valid method of investment appraisal.

13.3.1 Methods of evaluation

Appraisal methods basically fall into two categories which may be classed as (1) conventional methods and (2) discounting methods.

(1) Conventional methods
This term can be used to refer to the less complex methods which usually owe their simplicity to the fact that they do not take account of the timing of the cash flows arising from a project. Two such methods are considered here.

a) The pay-back method
The pay-back period of a project is the period it takes for the investment to recover its initial capital outlay in full.

Example

An investor has the choice of two mutually exclusive projects A and B with the following cash flows (£).

Year	0	1	2	3	4
Project A	−1000	500	500	100	100
Project B	−1000	400	400	400	400

(− indicates an outflow of funds)

Project A has a pay-back period of two years, but the investor would not recover his outlay from project B until the third year.

Project A is therefore the preferred project.

This method of appraisal is useful to the investor who is forced to emphasise the retention of his liquidity and needs his money back as soon as possible to put it to some other use. It is also attractive in industries subject to rapid technological advances, where plant may become obsolete and expectations of future returns are more uncertain. Its main drawback though, is its disregard of the returns that arise beyond the pay-back period – in the example, the point that the total returns from project B are £400 more than those from project A is ignored.

b) The average rate of return method

The average rate of return (ARR) on a project is found by taking the ratio of total returns to the capital outlay, averaged over the life of a project and expressed as a percentage.

Using the previous example

$$\text{ARR}_{\text{Project A}} = \frac{1200/1000}{4} \times 100 = 30\%$$

$$\text{ARR}_{\text{Project B}} = \frac{1600/1000}{4} \times 100 = 40\%$$

The purpose of the calculation is to find the project with the higher ARR, which is project B.

The fact that this method only considers the returns in aggregate and does not take account of their incidence is its major drawback.

(2) Discounting methods

The single factor, which distinguishes these methods from the previous, is that discounting methods of appraisal allow for the fact that money has a *'time value'*.

The time value of money. This expression refers to the ability of money to earn interest over time and the importance of the concept lies in the fact that any fixed sum of money varies in its value to a recipient, dependent upon the point in time in which it is received.

An investor, concerned with making comparisons between a capital sum which has to be laid out now and returns that arise next year, the year after that or ten years in the future, has to ensure that he is comparing sums on an equivalent basis.

Taking equivalent values
Compounding (i.e. taking account of compound interest) can be used for an illustration of the time value of money.

Example
£100 invested for three years at a rate of interest of 10% will accumulate at the end of each year as follows:

Year	0	1	2	3
Interested earned (£)	–	10	11	12.1
Total accumulated (£)	(Initial investment = £100)	110	121	133.1

Generally the following formula can be used: $A = P(1 + i/100)^n$
where A is the amount arising if a sum of money P is invested for n years at $i\%$.
For our example: $£100(1 + 0.1)^3 = £100(1.331) = £133.1$.

This shows that £100 in year 0 and £133.1 in year 3 are of equivalent value to an investor, if the going rate of interest is 10%.
From an investor's point of view, it is often more worthwhile though, to view this notion of equivalent values from a different viewpoint. He needs to make a comparison between a sum of money to be laid out now, and returns that occur in future years, and it is normally a more useful exercise to find the equivalent present value of the future sums. Such a process is termed discounting.

Discounting
The equivalent present value of a sum receivable in some future year can be calculated using the following formula:

$$PV = A(1 + i/100)^{-n}$$

where PV is the present value of an amount A in n years time, if the going rate of interest is $i\%$.

Example
For an income of £100 receivable in one year's time on an investment, if the going rate of interest is 10%, its present value is:

$$£100(1 + 0.1)^{-1} = £90.91$$

In other words, having £90.91 now is just as good as having £100 in one year's time to an investor who can invest his money at an interest rate of 10%.
We can look at two appraisal methods that incorporate this notion of discounting. This type of method usually being referred to as a discounted cash flow (DCF) technique.

a) The net present value (NPV) method
With this method, the forecast returns from a project are discounted to the period of the initial capital outlay, which is then subtracted, i.e. NPV = Present value of the returns less the capital outlay.

Example
A property company is considering a development project which requires an outlay of £90 000 and which will yield an estimated return of £30 000 for each of

the next four years. The going rate of interest is 10% which the company uses as its discount rate. The calculation of the NPV is shown below.

Year	Cash flow £ (a)	Discount factor 10% $= 1(1+0.1)^{-n}$ (b)	Present value £ $= (a) \times (b)$
0	−90 000	1	−90 000
1	30 000	0.9091	27 273
2	30 000	0.8265	24 795
3	30 000	0.7515	22 545
4	30 000	0.6831	20 493
		NPV =	+5 106

As the NPV is a +ve amount, this means that the project is viable and is worth undertaking. A simple way to understand this is to consider that if the company borrowed £95 106 at an interest rate of 10% and invested £90 000 in the project, it could keep the rest as 'profit' and the investment would pay for itself.

b) The internal rate of return (IRR) method
The IRR of a project is that rate of interest which, when used to discount the cash flow of a proposed project, reduces the NPV to zero.

For the cash flow of the development project in the previous example, the IRR must be greater than the 10% discount figure in order to reduce the NPV from £5106 to £0. The table below shows that the IRR must lie between a rate of 12% (NPV still +ve) and 13% (NPV now −ve).

Year	Cash flow £	Discount factor 12%	PV £	Discount factor 13%	PV £
0	−90 000	1	−90 000	1	−90 000
1	30 000	0.8929	26 787	0.8850	26 550
2	30 000	0.7972	23 916	0.7831	23 493
3	30 000	0.7118	21 354	0.6931	20 793
4	30 000	0.6355	19 066	0.6133	18 400
			NPV = +1 123		NPV = −764

By linear interpolation, the IRR works out to be 12.6% and as this is higher than the going rate of interest, the project is viable. An attraction of this method is that it is easy to understand.

The investor is presented with a rate of return which he can compare with the rate of interest on borrowed capital and if he has several alternative projects open to him, he can rank them in order for comparison.

For instance, if the IRR on project X is greater than that on project Y then, provided that it is more than the cost of capital, project X will be chosen. Generally, the project with the higher IRR is the one with the higher NPV and is therefore preferred under both methods.

Exercises

13.1 Two mutually exclusive investment projects X and Y have the following associated cash flows:

Year	0	1	2	3	4
Project X (£)	−80 000	40 000	30 000	20 000	10 000
Project Y (£)	−85 000	30 000	30 000	30 000	30 000

According to
a) the pay-back method
b) the average rate of return method
which should be the preferred project?

13.2 Two schemes have been suggested for the development of a particular site. The total costs of development for either scheme are the same but the building produced, the consequent rental income they will generate and the selling price when the property is sold after three years are different. The appropriate cost of capital for the company is 10%.
The estimated cash flows for the two schemes are as follows:

Year	0	1	2	3	4
Scheme A (£)	−1 000 000	100 000	100 000	100 000	1 200 000
Scheme B (£)	−1 000 000	50 000	70 000	90 000	1 300 000

Using the NPV appraisal method, indicate which scheme you consider would be the best to adopt.

13.3 Your client is considering the choice of alternative projects, whose costs and net cash proceeds are expected to be:

Year	Project A £	Project B £
0	−30 000	−32 000
1	5 000	20 000
2	10 000	15 000
3	15 000	15 000
4	20 000	10 000
5	20 000	5 000
	70 000	65 000

You are required to
a) calculate the Net Present Value of the projects at 10% rate of discount
b) determine the Internal Rate of Return of the projects
c) comment on the different ranking of the projects on the basis of NPV and IRR and advise your client on the choice of project.
You are given:

PV of £1

Year	at 10%	at 28%	at 29%	at 39%
1	0.9091	0.7813	0.7752	0.7194
2	0.8264	0.6104	0.6009	0.5176
3	0.7513	0.4768	0.4658	0.3724
4	0.6830	0.3725	0.3611	0.2679
5	0.6209	0.2910	0.2799	0.1927

13.4 The expenditure on a construction project can be distributed in two possible ways, as follows:

Year	0	1	2	3	4	5
Method 1	£300 000	NIL	50 000	NIL	50 000	NIL
Method 2	£200 000	40 000	40 000	40 000	40 000	40 000

If the present value factor is 10%, then use DCF techniques to decide which method to use.

13.5 a) What are the economic arguments for conducting a DCF analysis in the appraisal of capital projects?

b) Why is it particularly important that DCF analysis should be applied to property projects?

c) What differences would there be in the DCF analysis if the project was in the public rather than the private sector?

(ISVA)

Part Five

The Government and the Economy

14

Economic Objectives of Government

As we have seen in earlier chapters, there are economic problems to which a freely operating price system, left to its own devices, is unlikely to provide solutions. Given that there is a place for government involvement in the economy, we must look at the economic objectives of the government and consider the methods employed to achieve these objectives.

In the nineteenth century, the state was involved in providing only a few public services which people could not arrange for themselves – for example, national defence. The present century has, however, especially in the post-war period, witnessed a rapid growth in government involvement in the economy. The extent of this growth is reflected in the fact that even after a decade of government policies aimed at reducing the state's involvement in the economy, the state's share of total output in the economy was almost 40% in 1990.

14.1 A basic governmental policy aim: economic growth

Different governments may pursue various objectives with varying degrees of emphasis. In the mid-1960s for instance, the U.K. was suffering grave balance of payments problems and emphasis was placed on the achievement of a healthy trading position. Since the late 1960s a priority of governments has had to be the control of the upward trend in prices as inflation has been a major problem in the economy.

Policy objectives concerned with one particular problem can be considered later, because clearly, any government will have an underlying aim, which is to ensure that the best use is made of resources in the economy in order to ensure that the 'social welfare' of the country's population is as high as it can be. The way in which improvements in 'social welfare' are usually measured is by the degree of economic growth in the country.

The notion of economic growth is one that has already been mentioned in the opening chapter. An outward movement of an economy's production possibility curve indicates that the economy is able to produce more output than it could previously, and in simple terms, economic growth can be said to exist when there is an increase in the output produced by an economy over time. In recent history, inhabitants of the U.K. have experienced steady improvements in their economic well-being as a result of national economic growth.

A basic way to show such changes is to consider the increase in the total level of output in the economy from year to year. The value of all the extra output produced in a particular year in the economy expressed in money terms, is measured by the Gross National Product (GNP). Economic growth can be measured by the increase in the economy's level of output from year to year. Table 14.1 shows how the value of output in the U.K. increased in the late 1980s.

Table 14.1 GNP (at factor cost)

Year	£m
1985	309 368
1986	331 359
1987	362 089
1988	405 000
1989	443 356

(Source: Central Statistical Office)

It is, however, oversimplistic to assume that an increase in the size of the cake (i.e. the GNP) necessarily reflects a corresponding increase in social welfare. The value of output may have risen due to, for example, an increase in demand for luxury houses at the expense of building resources being used to construct say, hospitals. It may therefore be necessary to determine a concept of economic justice, and to evaluate one type of output against another. This would clearly spill over into the realms of politics and philosophy, and it is sufficient to point out here that if the GNP rises, then at least there is scope for a potential improvement in welfare as the capacity of the economy has expanded.

14.2 Policy objectives

In the light of the depression of the 1930s there has been a growing acceptance of the notion that the government has a vital role to play in the operation of the economy. Various governments in the post-war period have announced many different objectives which they hoped to accomplish, but basically – in addition to the pursuance of economic growth – they can be summarised as the attainment of:

1.   A low level of unemployment of especially human, but also other resources.
2.   Stability of prices, i.e. a low rate of inflation.
3.   A balance of payments equilibrium in our trade with the rest of the world.

The types of policy pursued by a government that wishes to reduce a balance of payments deficit will be looked at in a later chapter, but in this section, two of the major problems facing the U.K. economy, notably inflation and unemployment can be considered.

14.3 Demand management

The problems of inflation and unemployment basically result from inadequacies in the operation of the economic system.

If the demand for goods and services in the economy is not high enough to result in the economy's resources being fully utilised, then unemployment results, as firms have no need to hire extra labour, to purchase new capital equipment, to extend their premises or to purchase more materials. In the opposite case, if the demand for goods and services exceeds the ability of the economy to supply them, inflation results as prices are bid up by competing buyers.

If the economic evils of unemployment and inflation are to be avoided, the government's concern is that the total or aggregate demand for resources in the economy is at a level that produces an equilibrium level of production, which just ensures full employment. The failure of the system to prevent fluctuations in demand from this required level, has led to attempts by the government to step in and try to control demand. Such intervention is termed demand management.

Before examining specific governmental policies, it is necessary to examine how fluctuations in economic activity occur. This can be viewed by reference to ideas to put forward by John Maynard Keynes in his work *The General Theory of Employment, Interest and Money'* in 1936. He was writing on the economic problem that concerned people most in the 1930s – the depression. Traditional economic theory took the view that unemployment would not persist over a period of time, and Keynes concerned himself with an investigation of how the economy works to find the causes of – and, more importantly, a cure for – the unemployment problem. Some of his ideas and their implications for government economic policies to help stabilise economic fluctuations, are set out in the following sections.

14.4 The circular flow of income

As a starting point we can assume, rather simplistically, that we have a closed economy (i.e. there is no trade with the rest of the world) in which there is no government interference. There are two sectors in the economy notably *households*, who consume the goods and services produced by *businesses*, who

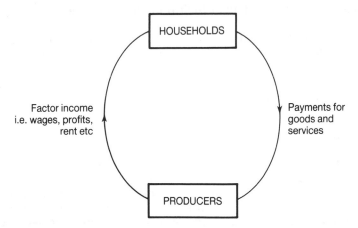

Fig. 14.1 A simple circular flow of income

in their turn, use this money to pay for the resources (factors of production) which they require to produce the goods. The factor incomes paid to the households, who sell their factor services to businesses, take the form of wages and salaries for the labour force, rents to land and property owners and interest and profits to the suppliers of capital. The relationship between the two sectors can be shown as a circular flow as in Fig. 14.1.

When the incomes of the individual households are totalled they show the *national income* which, from the firms' viewpoint, represents the total cost of producing the output of goods and services. *National product* is the total value of the output of all goods and services and so Fig 14.1 shows that the two flows must be equal.

Which comes first, consumer spending or income payments is a 'chicken and egg' argument. Economic activity is a continuous flow of goods and services induced by a counterflow of money spending originating from factor incomes.

In Fig. 14.1, if the total value of output was £xm, then factor incomes received must also be £xm, and this same amount of money would be spent on the goods produced (i.e. *national product = national income = national expenditure*). In other words, the same amount of income would be continuously flowing through the system without any change in its level.

This view of the economic system is obviously an oversimplified one, and several important factors have been omitted. The reasons why the level of income fluctuates, are to do with the fact that households dispose of their income in ways other than spending it all on the goods produced by firms, and producers also find that the demand for their output comes not just from consumers, but from other sources too.

14.4.1 Leakages and injections

The circular flow relationship between households and producers as shown in Fig. 14.1 is a direct one. We can now allow, though, for the fact that *leakages* take place from the flow in certain ways, which are:

a) The government takes away some income in the form of taxation, leaving households with less to spend.
b) Households do not spend all of their remaining income but save some of it instead.
c) Of the income that is spent on goods and services, a proportion does not go to home producers but is spent on imported goods and leaves the country.

Account also needs to be made of the various *injections* to the flow when demand arises from sources other than internal households. Basically, the injections arise from three sources:

d) The government spends the money it raises in taxes (or borrows) to ensure the provision of public services. Money must be spent on the every day running of these services and also to provide new capital such as roads, buildings etc.
e) Firms do not produce only consumer goods, but also capital goods (plant, equipment, buildings etc) which are purchased by other producers, who are thereby undertaking 'investment'. The money normally being borrowed from financial institutions, who channel savings in this direction.

f) There is a demand from abroad for goods and services produced in this country as foreign buyers spend money on our exports.

The original circular flow diagram can now be amended (Fig. 14.2) to show all these flows.

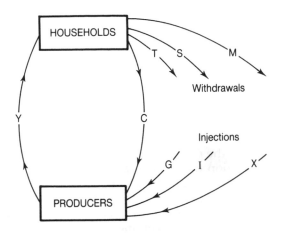

where Y = Total income
  C = Expenditure on (home produced) consumer goods
  T = Taxation
  G = Government spending
  S = Savings
  I = Expenditure on (home produced) capital goods by firms i.e. investment
  M = Spending on imported goods
  X = Demand for home-produced goods abroad i.e. exports

Fig. 14.2 The circular flow with withdrawals and injections

The flow of income is in equilibrium when the total leakages exactly equal the sum of the injections. This may be true in a case where the government spends just as much as it takes in tax, the banks cover their lending by customers' savings, and the nation's trade with the rest of the world balances.

Obviously, this position is merely hypothetical and the economy is constantly in a state of change in which the two sides do not balance. If the leakages outweigh the injections, the level of income will be reduced; but vice-versa, an increase in demand caused by the higher level of injections promotes expansion (if possible) in the economy.

14.4.2 A full employment level of income

As previously mentioned, Keynes' and his contemporaries' concern was to find a cure for the high level of unemployment prevailing at the time. There was not enough demand in the economy to produce a full employment level of income. Since government spending is one component of aggregate demand (in symbolic terms aggregate demand = C + G + I + X) and since the government can determine the level of its own spending, it follows that the government can affect the level of employment in the economy as a whole. Keynes' notion was that the country could spend its way out of the recession, and the government could take the lead in this by undertaking a public works spending programme, which would particularly stimulate demand in the construction industry. This boost to certain sectors of the economy would then provide a follow through expansion in demand in other sectors; the extent of this stimulus being determined by the 'National Income Multiplier' effect.

14.4.3 The concept of the Multiplier

An increase in the level of investment (public sector or private) in the economy is responsible for creating more employment than merely those jobs directly linked with the projects concerned. Take, for example, the case of government spending on a new large investment project such as a motorway. The cost of the project consists of wages paid to the workers, profits for the construction company, payments for materials etc. As explained previously, all this money must turn out as income accruing to someone.

The level of income in the economy would rise initially by an amount equal to the value of this injection to the flow, but this would not be the sole effect. Those people with the increased incomes spend some of this extra money on consumer goods, which is likely to create more employment in the relevant industries and give a further boost to overall incomes. As more transactions take place, this effect is multiplied even more.

14.4.4 An example of the Multiplier effect

The best way to understand how the Multiplier works, is to take a simplified example.

Assume that, owing to a new investment project, a worker receives an income of £10 000. Also, that he is faced with the choice of either spending this income on home-produced goods or else saving it, and, like everyone else in the economy, he chooses to spend 0.6 of his income and save the remaining 0.4. The proportion of this extra income (resulting from the project) which is spent, is referred to as the *'marginal propensity to consume'* and the proportion which is saved as the *'marginal propensity to save'*.

If the £6000 which this worker spends is received by one person, then this person in turn will spend £(0.6 × 6000) = £3600 out of this income. When this £3600 is then received as income by a third person, his expenditure will be £(0.6 × 3600) = £2160. This process could be carried on until the figures for extra income become negligible. We are interested in discovering what the overall value of all the incomes created is going to be. This could be calculated by adding together £(10 000 + 6000 + 3000 + 2160 + ... etc), but a far easier way to work out the total multiplied effect would be to use the following formula:

Total incomes created = Original increase in income × Multiplier, where:

$$\text{Multiplier} = \frac{1}{1 - \text{marginal propensity to consume}}.$$

Putting the appropriate values for the marginal propensity to consume from the example into the Multiplier formula, we have:

$$\text{Multiplier} = \frac{1}{1 - 0.6} = 2.5$$

This figure can now be used in the first equation:

Total incomes created $= £(10\,000 \times 2.5) = £25\,000$

This means that the initial creation of £10 000 of income from the investment results in an overall increase in income in the economy of £25 000.

In practice, the value of the Multiplier is reduced by the fact that the government will take away some of the increase in income in tax, and a further leakage occurs when part of the income is spent on imported goods. The greater the amount which goes in leakages, the smaller will be the Multiplier effect. For this reason, it may be said that a government wishing to promote growth in National Income may encourage spending (on home-produced goods and discouraging saving. The government is interested in the size of the Multiplier effect in order to gauge the extent to which any injections or withdrawals it promotes are likely to affect the economy.

The Multiplier effect shows the importance of investment in stimulating extra demand in the economy and thus promoting growth in National Income and employment. Conversely though, a fall in investment brings about a relatively larger reduction in National Income. The Multiplier effect works both ways.

14.4.5 Cyclical effects

The consequences of changes in investment on the level of income have so far been considered, but the other aspect of the relationship – the influence of income changes on investment must also be looked at.

When incomes rise, the demand for consumer goods inevitably increases, and the firms that produce such goods may have to invest in new plant, equipment and buildings to enable them to raise their output levels to meet this demand. Producers need to plan ahead and predict future demand, and so this investment must be in anticipation of such changes.

The principle underlying this idea is termed the *Accelerator*, which indicates that as consumer demand changes, the demand for capital (investment) rises or falls at a faster rate.

The building industry is probably the sector most affected by optimistic or pessimistic views of future demand held by producers of goods and services. The implications for planning in the building industry are that it must obviously be phased in anticipation of such changes.

14.4.6 Example of the Accelerator principle

In this example, the initial equilibrium level of income in the economy is 1000 (£ million) and the demand for consumer goods is 750. To produce these consumer goods, a stock of industrial buildings of 150 is required and 10% of this stock needs replacing each year.

Due to a rise in incomes to 1200 in year 4, it is expected that the demand for consumer goods will rise to 900 and consequently a buildings stock of 180 is needed by that year. This will have produced, therefore, a rise in investment in new building of 30 in year 3 in addition to the replacement of 15 to give a total of 45. In years 4 and 5 the replacement figure is 18 each year. Table 14.2 shows the changes mentioned and also the results of a further increase in income in year 7.

Table 14.2 The Accelerator principle

Year	Income	Consumer demand	Stock of industrial buildings	New building required (inc. replacement)
1	1000	750	150	15
2	1000	750	150	15
3	1000	750	150	45
4	1200	900	180	18
5	1200	900	180	18
6	1200	900	180	48
7	1400	1050	210	21
8	1400	1050	210	21

A relatively small increase in the level of demand for consumer goods (e.g. 20% in year 4) can cause a much greater temporary increase in the demand for building output (e.g. 200% in year 3). To cope with such changes and to avoid sudden shortages or surpluses, it is vital that the government monitors the demand for building work to a higher degree than is necessary for most other industries.

14.4.7 Aggregate demand and inflation

By the application of Keynesian ideas, governments had, until the early 1980s been able to avoid a high level of unemployment in the post-war period. Demand management policies have been used less successfully as methods of controlling inflation.

To understand the reason for this we can consider again the objective of a government trying to bring about full employment in the economy. An explanation of the government's aim is illustrated by Fig. 14.3.

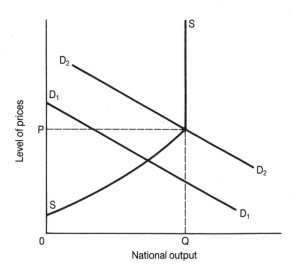

OQ = Level of output required to provide full employment

Fig. 14.3 Aggregate demand and supply

The diagram shows SS as the supply of resources forthcoming at different price levels. This supply curve is upward sloping to the point where the full employment of resources occurs; but when the level of prices rises above OP, the effect of further increases in demand can merely be to raise prices and produce inflation. (Unless of course new technology can improve the quality of resources, more human resources can be obtained by immigration or more capital goods produced at the expense of consumer goods, in which cases the supply curve would shift to the right.)

Successful demand management with the purpose of eliminating unemployment, should therefore aim to shift the aggregate demand curve from such a level of D_1D_1 to the level of D_2D_2 which would make for a full employment output and the optimum price level of OP.

14.5 A dual problem: unemployment with inflation

According to the theory put forward so far, it would appear that an economy can be faced either with a problem of unemployment (i.e. too low a level of aggregate demand) or with that of inflation (i.e. too high a level of demand) but not both.

Experience in many economies obviously belies this analysis. So what is the rational explanation of a situation where a high level of unemployment goes hand in hand with rising prices? The easy answer to the paradox is that these circumstances have arisen because the notion that supply and demand are constantly in equilibrium does not hold.

Consider the situation illustrated in Fig. 14.4.

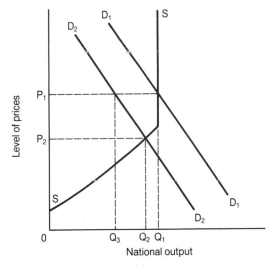

Fig. 14.4 The inflation-unemployment problem

Suppose that D_1D_1 is the original demand curve which, due to a deliberate action on the part of the government to reduce the level of inflation, shifts to D_2D_2 when there is a large cutback in public expenditure.

The effect of this reduction in demand should be a fall in output from OQ_1 to

OQ_2 resulting in correspondingly fewer workers being employed and a lowering of the price level from OP_1 to OP_2. The main problem with this interpretation is that it assumes that prices are responsive to such changes in demand. However, if both producers and households are conditioned to rising prices and rising wages, then trades unions will be reluctant to see their workers forced to accept reductions in their real incomes, and firms will be unwilling to lower their price increase expectations.

If prices were to stick, then what would result would be a reduction in output (and therefore employment) to a lower level than would otherwise occur. At the extreme, output may fall as far as OQ_3. Whilst the effect may not be quite as strong as this, the time period involved in reducing inflation in this way can bring about high levels of unemployment.

14.6 The national accounts

Data on U.K. aggregate economic activity is published annually. The flow of 'extra wealth' created in the economy in any one year can basically be measured in three separate ways. If the circular flow model is considered, then, by cutting through the flow at different points, the same overall flow should be measured.

Essentially, the three approaches to measuring this total income flow can be summarised as measurement of:

a) The total amount spent on final goods and services for consumption and investment. (Expenditure approach.)
b) The total cost of output in terms of the incomes of the factors used to produce it. (Income approach.)
c) The total value of the goods and services produced by the various industries and authorities. (Output approach.)

Each of these approaches can be looked at in turn.

14.6.1 Calculation of National Income in practice

Expenditure approach
The expenditure approach is the most important one to look at in detail. Table 14.3 shows the components of National Income in this method.

This approach involves the measurement of all categories of expenditure in the economy. The sum of consumers' expenditure, investment expenditure and general government final consumption is equal to Total Domestic Expenditure. Adding the value of total exports gives Total Final Expenditure. (Look at the symbolic $C + G + I + X$ in Fig. 14.2.)

Expenditure on imports represents an outflow of money from the U.K. and is deducted from Total Final Expenditure to arrive at the flow of total expenditure in the circular flow of income. This figure measures Gross Domestic Product (GDP) at market prices.

To measure GDP in terms of costs requires indirect taxes to be deducted and subsidies to be added to give GDP at factor cost. GDP is converted to Gross National Product (GNP) by adding net property income from abroad.

Table 14.3 National Income by category of expenditure

    Consumers' expenditure
+   General government final consumption
+   Investment expenditure (consisting of gross domestic fixed capital formation and value of physical increase in stocks)
    _____
=   Total Domestic Expenditure
+   Exports of goods and services
    _____
=   Total Final Expenditure
−   Imports of goods and services
    _____
=   Gross Domestic Product (GDP) at market prices
−   Taxes on expenditure
+   Subsidies
    _____
=   Gross Domestic Product (GDP) at factor cost
    _____
+   Net property income from abroad
    _____
=   Gross National Product (GNP)
−   Capital consumption
    _____
=   Net National product (NNP) or National Income (NI)

Finally, capital consumption (a measure of depreciation) is taken away to give Net National Product (NNP) or National Income.

Income approach
GDP and NI can also be calculated in terms of income. Total domestic income (TDI) is the sum of: all increases from employment and self-employment; gross trading profits of companies and gross trading surplus of public corporations and general government enterprises; rent; and other (imputed) incomes. Any increase in the money value of stocks (stocks appreciation) is deducted from TDI to give a measure of income attributable to activity in the current period. The resultant figure is GDP. (To reconcile this income-based measure of GDP with the expenditure-based measure, a residual error term is added. This is a statistical adjustment needed to balance the two measures.)
    Estimates of GNP and NNP (or NI) are then derived from it in exactly the same way as with the expenditure-based estimate.

Output approach
The outputs of the various goods and services industries in the economy are totalled (after an adjustment for financial services) to give an estimate of GDP and again, as with the income approach, GDP and NNP (or NI) can be derived.

The double-counting problem
To ensure that the national accounts give a true picture of income generated, care has to be taken that flows are not counted more than once in the measurement process. This problem has implications for each of the three approaches.
    The calculation of national expenditure mainly involves the collection of

market prices for goods and services, but what is required is the value of the national expenditure which corresponds to the cost of the factors of production used to produce the national product. Adjustments are therefore made for indirect taxes and subsidies. A basic premise is that higher VAT etc would give the government greater revenue and therefore boost government expenditure.

With the income approach, care must be taken to exclude transfer incomes, e.g. retirement pensions, student grants etc, as they represent a redistribution of income within society, and do not contribute to the creation of goods and services.

Finally, when calculating the values of national product it is only final expenditure which is measured. Intermediate sales, for example the value of purchases of glass and metal by glazing unit manufacturers, should not be included as the finished product would already include the value of these materials.

14.7 The 1980s: The Thatcher Years

During the 1980s, discussion of economic policy in Britain was dominated by 'Thatcherism', an economic doctrine that is wider in scope than the macroeconomy but which has particular relevance to it. Whilst demand management is consistent with either more or less involvement in economic life, Thatcherism was consistent only with less involvement. A reduction in government activity was one of the central tenets of this economic outlook. The ultimate objectives of government policy did not change; that is, the aim of achieving a high growth in living standards combined with stable prices, but what were distinctive were the methods of achieving them.

The two principle features were:

1.   The eradication of inflation was important not only for its own sake but also because of its effects on the level of unemployment in the long term. A major proposition being that inflation is a major cause of rising unemployment.
2.   Free market supply-side policies as the main weapon for tackling unemployment and raising the rate of growth of output. This broad notion of influencing the supply side of the economy has several facets:
Tax cuts to boost incentives.
A series of reforms in the labour markets.
Privatisation and deregulation to extract the State and its agencies from the economy.

Table 14.4 shows the degree of some of the more important privatisations of the period.

Table 14.4 Most notable U.K. privatisations (1981–90)

		% sold
1981	British Aerospace	56
1984	British Telecom	50.2
1986	British Gas	97
1987	British Airways	100
1988	British Steel	100
1990	Electricity Boards	100

14.7.1 Objectives of privatisation

The justification for this policy was based on several factors:

- Consumers were expected to benefit from rivalry, more choice and greater efficiency.
- Reduction of the size of the public sector through denationalisation.
- Reduction of public sector borrowing.
- A desire for wider share ownership.

Exercises

14.1 Explain why there are 3 methods of measuring National Income.

14.2 The consumption function in a particular economy is shown in the following table.

Income (£m)	Consumer expenditure (£m)
80 000	70 000
100 000	85 000
120 000	100 000
140 000	115 000
160 000	130 000

If this is a closed economy and there is no government interference, what is the equilibrium level of income if investment is £20 000m?

14.3 Complete the following table giving reasons for the insertions made. Assume a closed economy, with no government activity, that the marginal propensity to consume and average propensity to consume are constant and that in each period the economy is in equilibrium.

	Period I	Period II
National Income	£50 000m	
Consumption	£47 500m	£52 250m
Saving		
Investment		

Calculate the value of the multiplier.

(ISVA)

14.4 Given that the marginal propensity to consume is 0.8, describe the theoretical effect on the National Income of a cut of £1000 million in government spending.
State other factors which might, in practice, alter the real result of such a cut.

14.5 Examine the likely effect on the level of National Income of each of the following:
a) a rise in the level of taxation
b) a fall in the marginal propensity to save
c) a fall in exports.
Explain the process by which these effects take place, and consider each example separately.

14.6 Indicate, giving reasons, whether the following statements are true or false.
 a) Full employment is always achieved when National Income in equilibrium.
 b) Higher taxes cause National Income to fall.
 c) Increases in total spending cause the level of income to rise.
 d) When consumers save more of their income, they stimulate the economy and raise total spending and income.

14.7 Why, in a period when the level of National Income is below the full employment level, might an increase in the desire to save be discouraged?

14.8 What are the government's main economic policy objectives? Explain briefly why it might prove difficult to pursue all of these objectives simultaneously.

(ISVA)

14.9 From the items of expenditure, as listed in the National Accounts Summary Tables given below, indicate which are included to calculate each of the following measures at market prices:
 a) total fine expenditure;
 b) gross domestic product;
 c) gross national product;
 d) net national product;
 1. consumption
 2. general government expenditure (central and local authority)
 3. gross domestic fixed capital formation
 4. value of the physical increase in stocks
 5. exports
 6. imports
 7. net property income from abroad
 8. capital consumption

(ISVA)

14.10 a) Explain, using simple numerical examples, the following concepts:
 i)   marginal propensity to consume;
 ii) marginal propensity to save;
 iii) the Multiplier.
 b) Assume the government, in order to manage the economy, wishes to lower National Income from its present level of £400 billion to £320 billion and estimates that it can do so by reducing its own expenditure by £20 billion. Calculate, as estimated by the government:
 i) the marginal propensity to consume;
 ii) the value of the Multiplier.

(ISVA)

15

Fiscal Policy

The importance of government spending in the economy was considered in the previous chapter and so now attention can be paid to the main sources of the revenue used to finance this expenditure.

The sources of government revenue are shown in Table 15.1.

Table 15.1 Public income 1990/91

	Pence in every £
Income tax	25
National Insurance	16
Value Added Tax	15
Local authority rates and poll tax	11
Road fuel, tobacco and alcohol duties	10
Corporation tax (tax on company profits)	8
Capital taxes (taxes on the sale of assets)	3
Interest, dividends	3
Petroleum revenue tax and oil royalties	1
Other expenditure taxes	4
Other	4

(Source: CSO)

Whilst it may be the main objective of taxation to raise revenue, it can also serve other economic purposes. Governments have been raising finance through taxes for a long time – income tax for instance, was first introduced in this country in 1799 – but the use of taxation policy as a means of regulating the economy is a fairly recent phenomenon. It is only really in the post-war period that economic control by fiscal policy (i.e. management of the economy by variations in the levels and categories of taxation and public spending) has been of significance and nowadays, even if governments emphasise that their policy objectives revolve around monetary control, they must still rely on fiscal policy as well.

15.1 Types of tax

The government relies upon a variety of taxes for its revenue, but they can be categorised into two types as follows:

15.1.1 Direct taxes

These are taxes levied on income or capital and the most important of these, income tax, has for years been the largest, single revenue raiser. The more important direct taxes are:

a) Income tax. This is the most important element in the tax system. It is a tax payable on all income – earned income including bonuses and commissions, dividends, interest and rents. The way in which the tax system operates means that income earners receive a tax free allowance before they start to pay income tax but in periods of inflation the value of these allowances in real terms must fall. Also the tax is levied at a progressive rate which means that as incomes rise, the proportion of that income which is paid in tax rises more than proportionately. In the 1988 budget though, the Chancellor introduced a simplified two-rate structure with a standard and one higher rate.

   Whilst it is inevitable that income tax is a generally unpopular tax, from the government's viewpoint it is a tax whose increased yield at least keeps pace with inflation and it provides an excellent means of regulating the overall level of demand in the economy.

b) Corporation tax. This tax is levied on the profits of companies. The level of profits made by companies tends to be fairly volatile due to its dependence upon the state of boom or slump in the economy, and so the revenue collected by the government is also duly affected. In the early 1980s, numerous allowances could be made by companies when they undertook capital expenditure and the government only received a low yield from the tax. In 1980, for example, only 21% (on average) of industrial and commercial companies' gross trading profits were paid in tax even though the rate of corporation tax was 52% (for larger firms). In 1984 many of the allowances were removed and since that date the rate of tax has been greatly reduced.

c) Capital gains tax. A tax applied to gains accruing from the disposal of assets. The gains may be purely paper ones as well as personal possessions but there are certain exemptions, the most important of which are private residences. Capital gains tax has been index-linked since 1982 so that only real gains are taxed.

d) Inheritance tax. Inheritance taxes have been levied in the U.K. since 1894, but since 1986 this has been the official title of this tax on the transfer of wealth.

15.1.2 Indirect taxes

Into this category fall the various types of tax on expenditure. A tax may be levied generally on a wide-ranging assortment of goods and services (such as Value Added Tax) or it may be applied just to one type of spending in particular (such as a betting tax). The main indirect taxes are:

a) Value Added Tax. This is basically a general turnover tax on the consumption of goods and services. It was introduced in 1973 ostensibly to simplify the system of indirect taxation but also to bring this country into line with European Community practice. V.A.T. is an *'ad valorem'* tax which means that it is levied as a percentage of the value of the item and it is consequently, an inflation-proof tax from the government's viewpoint, i.e. as the price of the good goes up due to inflation, so the revenue received by the government from the tax goes up at the same rate. Another important aspect is that V.A.T. is rebated on exports but is added to the price of imported goods.

b) Other expenditure taxes: Whilst V.A.T. may be the main revenue raiser in this category, other less general expenditure taxes are often quite lucrative sources of tax revenue for the Exchequer. This revenue comes mainly from taxes and duties on smoking, gambling, alcoholic drinks and from motoring (from petrol, oil, motor vehicle duty and car tax). Such taxes are often levied as *'specific duties'*, i.e. charged as a fixed amount and their real value falls in times of inflation unless the duties are raised – the need for constant revaluation enhancing the public unpopularity of these duties. The goods involved are usually goods with a very low elasticity of demand (often habit goods) and are considered to be non-essential goods, even though expenditure on alcohol, tobacco and gambling may account for a larger proportion of low-income budgets than high-income budgets.

15.2 Government spending

The ways in which the government spends the money it raises show how it influences the different sectors of the economy. Public spending has been a growth industry in Britain for many years. Even the Conservative governments of the 1980s with a commitment to try to decrease the level of the public sector, found that it is difficult to reduce public expenditure once it has taken root. The areas of this public expenditure in 1990–91 are shown in Table 15.2.

Table 15.2 Public expenditure 1990/91

	Pence in every £
Social security	25.5
Health	12
Education and science	9.5
Defence	4.5
Law and order	3
Transport	18
Other services	9
Interest on the national debt	3.5
Repayment of part of the national debt	3
Other	12

(Source: CSO)

This expenditure is carried out by three types of body – central government, local government and the nationalised industries and public corporations. About 60% of the total is undertaken directly by central government, 30% by local authorities and the rest by the nationalised industries and public corporations.

Perhaps the most important way to break down the expenditure though, is to split it into:

a) *Expenditure on capital investment* – roads, school buildings, hospitals, houses, plant and buildings for public sector industry etc.
b) *Current consumption expenditure* – salaries, subsidies, grants, interest on debt etc.

It is normally assumed that capital expenditure is beneficial because it enhances the productive capacity of the economy, but current expenditure may not directly do so.

One concern with capital investment in the public sector is that it should yield as high a return as would be obtained in the private sector. As already mentioned in the chapter on the construction industry, local authority direct works departments have to obtain a rate of return on their capital supposedly comparable to that being earned in the private sector, and a similar criterion applies to the nationalised industries. The notion is that the opportunity cost – what resources could earn if left in private hands – of public investment must be taken into account.

15.3 Cutbacks in government spending

It is an unfortunate fact that when government, at both central and local level, wishes to reduce its expenditure it is usually capital spending that bears the brunt of the attack.

Decisions to reduce investment will mainly affect future generations where-as reductions in current services are felt straight away. Authorities find it easier – and perhaps less politically unpopular – to scrap or postpone an expensive future project than to reduce services and perhaps make workers immediately redundant. A local authority for example, may be forced to put off new house building but may maintain or even step up its direct works department's activity on repairs and maintenance of the existing housing stock.

Obviously the construction industry is the one most affected by cutbacks in new road construction, council house building and other public sector con-struction work such as schools, hospitals etc. Conversely though, just as construction is the vanguard industry during the recession in public sector spending, when policy changes, the development of most services such as housing, education and public sector industry must inevitably begin with a take-off in the demand for building services.

15.4 Effects of general economic policy on the building industry

In its attempts to regulate the economy, the government pursues policies to attain general objectives such as the maintenance of full employment, control of the level of inflation etc. These policies obviously have repercussions upon the construction industry.

For example, if the government were successful in raising the level of real income, then speculative housebuilders would find it easier to sell their products, compared to a situation in which income was falling and unemploy-ment increasing. When the government finds it necessary to cut back on expansion because of inflationary dangers, construction firms are likely to experience a drop in the demand for their services.

Both fiscal and monetary measures give the government an important degree of control over the private sector of the economy and their effects on the level of investment are important for the industry. Investment expenditure is a strategic component of aggregate demand and construction activity accounts for a major part of investment – approximately one half of the gross annual fixed capital formation of the U.K. It is therefore, worth considering the way in which general government measures influence construction activity.

15.5 Fiscal measures

Fiscal measures have been especially important in the post-Keynesian era as means of stimulating the level of activity in the economy.

In a full-employment situation, if government action were to attempt to boost the economy and the demand for construction work rose, then in the short-run the effects would be inflationary in the industry as wages and materials prices were bid up.

With the decline in overall government spending in the 1980s, the construction industry was one of the main industries to suffer due to its dependence on the public sector. Whenever government departments and local authorities are undertaking cutbacks it tends to be reductions in capital expenditure that occur first, i.e. less expenditure on roads, houses, schools etc. As an example Table 15.3 shows how the value of new housing work for the public sector (after taking account of inflation) fell during the period 1988–90.

Table 15.3 Value of output: New housing work in the public sector (at 1985 prices)

	£m
1988	789
1989	754
1990	706

(Source: Housing and Construction Statistics)

However, when measures such as grants for industrial development are undertaken by the government to regenerate industry or whenever social policy is expanded and more resources devoted to education, the health service etc, the construction industry is one of the first to benefit from the increased spending.

15.6 The effects of taxation

Taxes may be designed to limit the volume of new construction activity, but general increases in tax rates may also reduce the demand for construction either directly or indirectly. For example, an increase in the rate of tax levied on income receivable from property or profits from using property may lead to a decrease in the demand for new construction. Tax concessions may also be important factors – especially the mortgage interest tax relief for house purchasers.

A general increase in tax, such as a rise in income tax rates is likely to reduce the demand for goods generally. This would have an accelerator effect on a firm's demand for new plant and buildings, and plans for premises extensions may well be shelved.

Exercises

15.1 Why does the government raise its revenue by both direct and indirect taxes?

15.2 What would be the likely effects on the level of construction activity in the economy of:
   a) direct subsidies for private housebuilders?
   b) a tax on the holding of undeveloped land?
   c) a reduction in the general level of income tax?

15.3 An individual's weekly income rises from £150 to £180 and he consequently pays more tax.
   If the amount of tax he pays changes
   a) from £30 to £37.50.
   b) from £15 to £17.
   c) from £30 to £67.50.
   d) from £75 to £90.
   Calculate his (i) marginal tax rate and (ii) original and (iii) final average tax rates. Comment on your findings.

16

Monetary Policy

The use of fiscal policy by the government as a means of managing demand in the economy was considered in the previous chapter. An alternative, or usually complementary, method of control involves measures affecting the quantity or price of money in the economy. This is termed monetary policy. When people have more money they tend to spend more and conversely a fall in the amount of money in the economy is likely to reduce the overall level of demand.

16.1 The functions of money

The starting point in an appraisal of monetary policy must be a definition of money. Basically anything that performs the functions of money *is* money. There are three such interrelated functions.
1.   The foremost is that money acts as a medium of exchange. It is used to buy goods and services, and sellers accept it as a means of payment. Without an accepted means of exchange, the economy would have to rely on a barter or direct exchange system, and the problems that this would involve would seriously handicap the whole economy. A farmer who wanted a new house may have to find a builder who needed two hundred sheep in exchange!
2.   Money also acts as a standard of value. It enables the relative worth of various goods and services to be compared. Money is the common denominator for expressing this worth and for quoting prices. For example, the price of a house does not have to be quoted in terms of sheep, cars, cigarettes or any other product.
3.   Finally, money is a store of value. It is the most liquid of all assets and can be used to buy goods in whatever amounts the purchaser chooses, whenever he chooses. It is therefore an extremely convenient way of storing wealth.
   There are, however, disadvantages in storing wealth in this form. The holder loses out on interest which could have been earned if the assets had been held in some other form. Furthermore, the purchasing power of money falls in periods of inflation.

16.2 The characteristics of money

To perform the aforementioned functions properly, it is important that the money used in an economy has certain characteristics. Notably:

a) *Acceptability.*   If money is to be used as a medium of exchange then the

currency must be acceptable to everyone in the economy. They must have faith in the body issuing the money, i.e. the government.
b) *Divisibility.*   So that transactions of different sizes can be carried out.
c) *Portability.*   To make it easier to use money.
d) *Durability.*   Money should have a useful life.
e) *Stability.*   An important consideration if money is to be used as a store of wealth. The inability of governments in the past to control inflation has produced the collapse of economies.

16.3 The demand for money

This refers to the desire to hold money rather than have it tied up in bank accounts, building society deposits and so on.
    According to Keynes, there are three types of demand for money:

1.   *The transactions demand.* People need a certain amount of money to meet their everyday needs for goods and services all kinds. The extent to which money is held for this motive, depends firstly on the size of the gap between the time when money is received and when it is spent, and secondly upon the level of income in the economy, as when incomes are rising, households tend to increase their demand for money.
2.   *The precautionary demand.* This type of demand arises from uncertainty. People are never certain what payments they may have to make in the future, and arm themselves with extra money on top of that required to meet their normal needs to cover unknown eventualities. The same factors are likely to determine the level of this demand as affect the transactions demand.

    The demand to hold money for both these reasons is referred to as the demand for *'active balances'*.

3.   *The speculative demand.* The higher the level of interest rates in the economy, the greater the opportunity cost of holding money and thus the lower the desire to hold money. Conversely, if interest rates are presently low but are expected to rise, people choose to hold money instead of using it to buy securities or bonds.

    The *'idle balances'* which people hold are therefore related to the level of interest rates.
    Overall, the demand for money is affected by the level of national income and by the level of interest rates in the economy.
    The demand for money, together with the supply, determines the level of interest rates which in a sense relates the 'price' of holding money, i.e. the opportunity cost involved.

16.4 The money supply

Whilst the notes and coins in circulation constitute the basis of the money supply in our economy, the majority of transactions are not conducted through the medium of cash. Goods and services are instead paid for by transferring claims on the banking system. In other words, a definition of the money supply can include the value of bank deposits.

16.4.1 Official definitions

Definitions of the money supply vary according to the degree of liquidity involved, i.e. how easily an asset can be transferred from one use to another. The most liquid assets make up the narrowest definition of money and consist of notes and coins in circulation.

Wider definitions include broader interpretations of savings and deposit accounts, and terminology ranges from the narrowest definition (M0) to the broadest (M5). The official definitions of the money supply have altered many times over recent years. The reason for the multiplicity of definitions is that it is not clear in practice which institutions are banks. A building society is treated as a bank for some definitions but not for others. The Abbey National's conversion to a bank in 1989 triggered an alteration in definitions of money because it caused a huge switch of assets from the building society to the banking sector.

One chosen target for concern is now M0 which consists of notes and coins held by the public and banks plus banks' holdings and their balances at the Bank of England. M5 is the broadest measure and takes money in its widest context to include building society deposits and private sector holdings of bank bills, Treasury bills etc. The total money stock by these two definitions is shown in Table 16.1

Table 16.1 Money Stock

Year	M0 (£m)	M5 (£m)
1985	11 095	239 365
1986	14 665	276 203
1987	16 338	319 307
1988	16 402	372 452
1989	17 334	439 850
1990	18 126	508 221

(Source: Bank of England)

16.5 Banks and credit creation

The greater part of the money supply therefore consists of figures in bank accounts and the creation of such money is a major function of the commercial banking system. The way in which the banks are able to create money is by taking in deposits from savers and then making a loan to another customer with this money. The system functions in this way because the banks know that not all their customers are going to want their money back (as cash) at the same time, and so they only need to keep a relatively small percentage of money in this form. This means that banks are able to keep a proportionately small ratio of their assets in cash and make potential loans on the basis of the rest.

16.5.1 The creation of credit

Banks obviously need to hold enough cash to meet their customers' demand for cash withdrawals, but let us assume that they have discovered from experience that this need only amount to 10% of their total deposits.

If person A deposits £10 000 at a bank, then the bank may lend out £9000 to customer B and retain the other £1000 as cash.

When person B spends the £9000, by perhaps giving person C a cheque for £9000 when purchasing a car, the £9000 will be deposited in a bank who will keep £900 as cash, and create new credit of £8100 for customer D.

This process will continue until effectively £100 000 worth of deposits are created.

This figure could have been calculated by application of the *deposit to cash (or credit) multiplier*:

$$\frac{1}{\text{Cash (or reserve asset) ratio}}$$

i.e. Original deposit × ratio = Total deposits created
£10 000   × 10   = £100 000

This simplified notion of credit creation being based on cash reserves explains the basic principles involved. However, in practice, it is the general liquidity position of the banks not just cash, which affects lending policies.

16.6 Monetary control

The fact that governments are concerned with controlling the supply of money recognises the important role which money has to play in the operation of the economy. Monetary policy, which can be defined simply as the maintenance of control of the money stock, must nowadays be an important part of the government's strategy.

16.7 Money and inflation

The purpose behind a policy based on monetary control lies in the relationship between money and prices. Growth in the money supply is seen by some economists (termed Monetarists) to be the major cause of inflation in the economy. Inflation can be defined as a general rise in price levels or as a fall in the value of money. A basic premise views such a fall in value as the result of an excess supply of the commodity 'money'.

In the U.K. in the 1970s there were large increases in the availability of credit in the economy. Credit was made relatively freely available both for companies and for consumers with the relaxation of controls on bank lending, with a resultant double-figure inflation rate by the end of the decade.

An accepted measure of inflation is the annual increase in the Retail Price Index (RPI). Table 16.2 shows how the RPI changed in the period up to 1990 as inflation gradually came under control.

Table 16.2 Index of Retail Prices

	Index (Annual Average)	
1984	89.2	
1985	94.6	
1986	97.8	
1987	101.9	(13 January 1987 = 100)
1988	106.9	
1989	115.2	
1990	121.3	

(Source: CSO Economic Trends)

16.7.1 Control of the money supply

In the 1980s the main priority of government policy was the elimination of inflation, and effective control of the rate of growth of the money supply was seen as one of the main means of achieving this objective.

Fig. 16.1 shows the relationship between one measure of the money stock (M3) and the rate of change in the Retail Price Index since 1964.

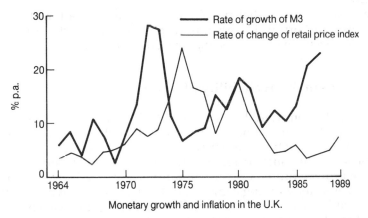

Monetary growth and inflation in the U.K.

Fig. 16.1 Interest rate policy

In recent years a high interest rate policy has been adopted in an attempt to stem what has been perceived as an excessive inflation rate.

The Bank of England adjusts the supply of credit by influencing the short-term rate of interest. High interest rates increase the cost of borrowing and expensive credit deters would-be spenders in all sectors. Whilst reductions in consumer spending might, at times, be economically desirable to control inflation, the effects of high interest rates on investment can cause many problems to businesses.

16.8 The effects of monetary policy on the construction industry

If monetary control is to be used as a basis for reducing the level of inflation in the economy then, as has been shown, the policy can have two facets.

Government policy can affect both the cost of borrowing (for the construction industry and its customers) and also the availability of credit. These two factors can be considered separately.

16.8.1 Changes in the level of interest rates

If the government were pursuing an anti-inflationary policy and succeeded in raising interest rates, what would be the effect on construction activity?

In the short-term, for buildings under construction, the developer will probably be willing to pay high rates of interest to obtain the necessary finance to finish the building, as the part-finished building is earning no income. Those construction firms with overdrafts have increased costs and will probably be forced to reduce their stocks of materials.

In the long-term, the demand for construction activity will fall as the profitability of construction will be lower and purchasers may experience difficulties in obtaining finance as a result of the higher interest rates. Higher prices for construction work not yet started may lead to the postponement or abandonment of a building, dependent on the stage reached. For projects in the planning stage, poorer materials may be used and smaller buildings constructed.

Another major factor is that people may be unable to afford to pay higher interest rates and borrow large sums to purchase property. Some projects, especially for speculative builders, may become unprofitable.

16.8.2 Changes in the availability of credit

Again, this can be considered in the context of a government trying to reduce the level of activity in the economy. If credit is difficult to obtain, this is likely to affect the level of construction activity to a greater extent than a change in interest rates. Actual construction and the purchase of property both depend heavily on borrowed funds. Construction firms rely greatly on overdrafts from commercial banks for working capital and the smaller firms without alternative sources would be worst hit. The overall reduction in the availability of loans would lead to a lower level of construction activity.

Exercises

16.1 Explain what is likely to happen to the demand by households for precautionary money balances if:
a) national income declines.
b) wages and salaries are paid at more frequent intervals.
c) people become more optimistic.

(ISVA)

16.2 The total supply of money in an economy is £24 000 million. The demand for money for financing current spending transactions is £8000 million. The demand for money to hold as an asset varies with the general rate of interest as shown below.

Rate of interest (per cent)	7	6	5	4
Demand for asset money (£)	8000	16 000	28 000	44 000

a) What will be the rate of interest in this economy?

b) If the government took steps to reduce the money supply to £16 000 million, what would be the effect on the rate of interest?

c) If as a result of b), business activity decreased, how and why do you think the rate of interest might be affected?

(ISVA)

16.3 A banking system is required to keep a 12½% cash ratio. Indicate the change in the money supply if the government

a) sells £1000 million of securities.

b) redeems £2000 million of securities.

c) reduces the cash ratio requirement to 10%.

Answer each question starting from the initial position.

Assume that the banks create credit to the full extent allowed, and that all transactions pass through banking accounts.

(ISVA)

16.4 Examine the limitations on the power of commercial banks to advance loans to their customers.

17

The U.K. Economy in an International Context

17.1 The reasons for trading overseas

Britain has for centuries figured prominently amongst the world's trading nations, and there must obviously be many advantages that make it worthwhile for the country to trade with other nations.

The main reason that countries trade with one another rather than try to run totally independent economies, is that resources are not equally distributed between countries. Virtually no country in the world is in a position to be self-supporting and the U.K., with its scarcity of many natural resources, needs to obtain vital commodities from overseas. It is consequently easy to understand how the U.K. gains from exchanging manufactured goods for such materials as copper, tin, crude rubber, timber etc, as well as a whole variety of foodstuffs. Some commodities just could not be produced in the U.K. and there are others which could not be produced in sufficient quantities or only at considerable expense here.

The gain from this type of trade is obvious; the population is able to enjoy the benefits from commodities otherwise unobtainable. Yet when we import steel, textiles, cars and other things that British workers can and do produce, people become confused. If we can produce these items ourselves, how can we gain from buying abroad?

One argument for allowing such competition from abroad is that the stimulation developed in the economy tends to reduce the dangers of monopoly forming. The competition forces home producers to achieve greater efficiency and keep their prices as low as possible in order to maintain their share of the market.

17.2 Specialisation

The advantages associated with specialisation have already been mentioned in previous chapters, but it is worth considering a specific example in the context of international trade.

Assume two countries X and Y can each produce timber and steel, but X has a climate which is ideally suited for growing timber and Y has the advantage of an industrially trained workforce. Consequently, if each country devoted a half of its resources to both timber and steel production, X could produce 60 units of timber and 30 units of steel and Y could produce 40 units of timber and 70 units of steel.

Total output of timber and steel would both be 100 units. Yet if both countries specialised according to their strengths, even with only constant returns to scale in both types of production, X's output of timber would be $(60 \times 2 =)$ 120 units and Y's output of steel $(70 \times 2 =)$ 140 units. The production possibility curves in Fig. 17.1 illustrate these figures.

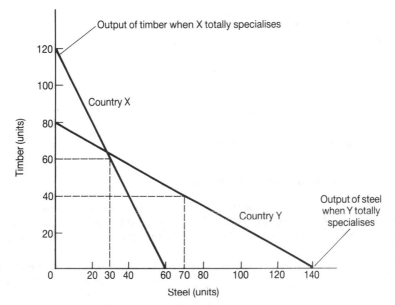

Fig. 17.1 Specialisation and international trade

In other words, the total outputs of each commodity would increase, and the two countries should quite easily be able to come to a trading agreement whereby both benefit from the overall improvement.

17.3 Comparative advantage

In spite of such benefits, most countries try to provide some of their basic necessities themselves, so as not to be totally dependent on others.

However, some countries are in a position where they can produce many products more cheaply and efficiently than the rest of the world. This does not mean though, that the less-efficient countries should merely purchase all their requirements from the more-efficient ones and produce nothing themselves. The more-efficient should concentrate on the production of those goods for which they have the *greater comparative advantage*, and the less-efficient countries should produce those goods in which they have the *lesser comparative disadvantage* according to the *theory of comparative costs*.

Returning to our example, assume now that one country (X) has both the better climate and the industrially trained workforce.

Fig. 17.2 illustrates the combinations of the two commodities which each country could now produce.

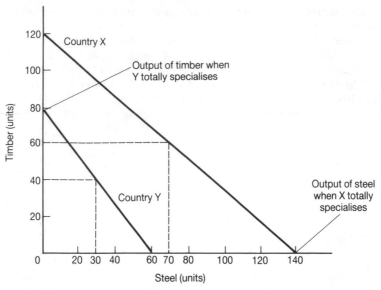

Fig. 17.2 Comparative advantage and specialisation

Now if X and Y each used a half of their resources to produce timber and steel, then X could produce 70 units of steel and 60 units of timber and Y could produce 30 units of steel and 40 of timber. Total production would be 100 units of steel and 100 units of timber.

Yet if X used all its resources to produce steel and Y did the same for timber, it could be shown that there are overall benefits from specialisation and trading.

Table 17.1 shows the initial, post-specialisation and post-trading position after the two countries have agreed to exchange 60 units of steel for 60 units of timber, i.e. the *'terms of trade'* are 1:1, steel for timber.

Table 17.1 Trading according to comparative advantage

	Steel	Timber	
X	70	60	
Y	30	40	Initial position
TOTAL	100	100	

	Steel	Timber	
X	140	0	Post-specialisation position
Y	0	80	
TOTAL	140	80	

	Steel	Timber	
X	80	60	Post-trade position
Y	60	20	
TOTAL	140	80	

Compared to the original situation, country X is obviously 'better off' to the tune of 10 units of steel. But how about country Y? If other countries were still willing to exchange steel for timber at a rate of 1:1, country Y could more than restore its status quo by trading steel for timber now. Even if this were not the case though, Y has gained 30 units of steel which it would require the productive output of one quarter of its resources to produce and has lost 20 units of timber, again equivalent to the output of a quarter of its resources. In other words, it would at least break-even, thus leaving an overall gain for the two countries combined.

17.4 Interference with trade

In these theoretical examples there can be seen to be clear-cut advantages to be gained from a system of free (i.e. unrestricted) trade between countries. The virtues of freedom of trade are extolled by various international organisations, notably the International Monetary Fund (IMF), and in the post-war period the General Agreement on Tariffs and Trade (GATT) was formed with the intention of removing barriers to trade.

Yet despite the benefits of such a policy, virtually every country in the world forsakes free trade in favour of trade protection. This protection of home producers can take various forms, such as import tariffs, restrictions on the number of goods from abroad, subsidies for home producers to make their goods more competitive etc. There are several reasons for such actions, notably:

a) The removal of competition from abroad by import quotas or tariffs is often used when a country wishes to help infant industries, which in their early stages of development are at a cost disadvantage compared to their established competitors from abroad.

b) The maintenance of employment in domestic industries may be en-dangered by cheap imports. This may be the result of cheap labour or cheap materials used by foreign manufacturers, or it may arise from a policy of 'dumping', where the exporter sells his surplus goods abroad at an uneconomically low price in order to preserve his home market. This unfair competition must justifiably be guarded against.

c) Strategic tariffs are imposed to protect those industries whose products may be essential in time of crisis. For instance, many industrialised countries protect their farming industries in order to ensure food supplies. Countries often also wish to preserve indigenous sources of energy and may force consumers to pay high prices, inflated by import tariffs for oil and other fuels.

d) Finally, a country may wish to cut back on its expenditure on imports if it is not selling enough of its own goods abroad to pay for them. Raising the prices of these imports by the imposition of tariffs to make the goods unattractive to home consumers, or restrictions on the quantity imported, are means of correcting a balance of payments problem.

17.5 The balance of payments

Having considered why countries trade with each other it is now pertinent to examine how the U.K. assesses the value of its trade. The measurement of this trade with the rest of the world is laid out in a set of accounts termed the balance of payments, which together can be defined as a systematic annual record of the U.K.'s trade and other financial transactions with the rest of the world.

17.5.1 The current account

This account summarises the U.K.'s transactions with the rest of the world and is divided into two parts; one showing the value of goods imported and exported, and the other showing invisibles which refer to the purchase and sales of services.

Table 17.2 shows the U.K.'s current account summary figures for the period 1985–89.

Table 7.2 U.K. balance of payments on current account

	1985	1986	1987	1988	£m 1989
Visible trade					
Exports	77 991	79 656	79 446	80 776	92 792
Imports	81 336	82 141	90 669	101 854	116 632
(a) Visible balance	−3 345	−9 485	−11 223	−21 078	−23 840
Invisibles					
Credits	80 157	77 248	79 855	88 168	109 098
Debits	74 062	67 787	72 814	82 241	104 384
(b) Invisible balance	6 095	9 462	7 042	5 927	4 714
(a) + (b) CURRENT BALANCE	2 750	−24	−4 182	−15 751	−19 126

(Source: CSO)

The difference between the value of the goods exported and those imported is termed the *visible balance* or *'balance of trade'* and this must be added to the *invisible balance* to give the overall current balance.

In the post-war period, prior to the development of the U.K. North Sea oil industry, there have been few occasions on which the U.K. has shown a surplus on its visible trade and the U.K. has had to rely on the invisible sector as the stronger part of its trade dealings.

17.6 Composition of U.K. trade

The U.K. has traditionally been an importer of raw materials and exporter of manufactured goods but Table 17.3 shows that there have been significant changes in the trade pattern over recent decades. However, such a switch towards European markets since the 1970s has meant that raw materials now constitute a much smaller proportion of imports than they previously did, and the decline in the country's manufacturing base in the 1980s inevitably led to a need to import more finished products.

The growth area in terms of exports has been that of oil due to the development of the North Sea oil industry, and there have been significant changes in manufactured exports with a continued growth in chemical products and steady decline in engineering products.

Table 17.3 Commodity analysis of U.K. visible trade

	% total value				
Exports	*1970*	*1975*	*1980*	*1985*	*1990*
Food etc & basic materials	9.4	9.8	9.9	9.0	10.2
Fuels	2.2	4.2	13.6	21.5	11.8
Semi-manufactured	32.4	31.2	29.6	25.6	28.8
Finished manufactured	50.2	51.0	44.0	41.2	47.6
Imports	*1970*	*1975*	*1980*	*1985*	*1990*
Food etc & basic materials	36.3	26.4	19.6	16.6	15.6
Fuels	8.3	17.5	14.2	12.8	5.4
Semi-manufactured	29.2	23.9	27.3	24.8	26.8
Finished manufactured	24.6	29.9	36.6	44.0	50.2

(Note: The annual totals are less than 100% owing to a small proportion of unclassified commodities)
(Source: Annual Abstract of Statistics)

If the U.K. had been forced to rely on its trade in physical goods over the years, the country would have gone deeper and deeper into debt. Fortunately, the country has always been able to rely on the fact that it is a net exporter of services.

Invisible credits arise in several ways. For instance, the British insurance industry (especially Lloyds) provides its services all over the world; British banks receive profits from their international banking services; British shipping and airline companies carry foreign freight and passengers; foreign tourists visit this country and spend their money here. In a similar manner, invisible debits occur from such factors as British tourists holidaying abroad or profits earned by foreign companies in the U.K. being returned to their home country.

17.6.1 Capital account

Not all international payments that occur between countries are in exchange for goods and services. If the British government or a U.K. citizen or company invests abroad then money is leaving the U.K. economy. Similarly, money is transferred to the U.K. if, for instance, a U.S. oil company invests in a North Sea oil project or a Japanese car company sets up a new plant here.

To find the total flow of funds between the U.K. and other countries, the balance of the capital account must be added to the current account balance.

A critical factor affecting the flow of capital funds into the U.K. in recent years has been the level of interest rates in this country compared to that overseas. These flows, however, may for the most part be very short-term (colloquially termed 'hot money').

A balance of payments deficit
Any country, which finds itself in a situation where it is constantly in deficit on its balance of payments accounts, can only sustain such deficits by borrowing or drawing on its reserves for a limited period. There may be specific reasons for a disequilibrium in a particular year, but generally solutions to this type of problem involve measures designed to reduce the net outflow of currency from the U.K.

Such measures may include:

a) The imposition of tariffs to raise the price of imported goods and make them less attractive, or the use of quota restrictions (on foreign cars for instance) to reduce the volume of imports.

b) Control of domestic inflation in order to make the prices of home-produced goods more competitive at home and also in export markets.

c) The monetary authorities can introduce exchange control regulations. Limits may be put on the amount of foreign currency that travellers spend abroad or the amount which nationals are able to invest abroad.

d) Depreciation of the currency exchange rate. An effective method of altering expenditure patterns – to encourage foreigners to spend more on British exports and Britons to spend less on imports – is to alter the relative prices of imports and home-produced goods. British exports can be made more competitive by lowering the rate at which the pound exchanges for foreign currencies. Because fewer units of their currency have now to be given up to obtain sterling, foreigners can buy British goods more cheaply. Also, Britons find that foreign goods are more expensive compared to home-produced goods with the result that import demand is reduced.

Consequently, provided that a degree of competition exists and the demand for both imports and exports is sufficiently elastic, a correction of the balance of payments deficit should occur. Such corrective exchange-rate adjustments should occur automatically through a freely operating exchange rate system.

17.7 The export performance of the building industry

When there is a recession in building work, some contractors, as might be expected, look abroad for work. In the 1970s and 1980s the British construction industry took advantage of the increased demand from abroad for building services, and a proportion of the U.K.'s invisible earnings arose from work undertaken by building consultants and contractors.

The most important market areas for the U.K. construction industry have been the Middle East and African countries, where British success in the export field is based on its imperial past. Much of the work tends to be undertaken by a small number of larger firms, who provide the management expertise and key staff for projects.

Linked to the increased export of building services has been the growth in overseas markets for construction materials and equipment. In fact, the export of materials and components tends to make a larger contribution to the balance of payments than contractors and consultants put together.

17.8 The European Community

In 1972 the British Parliament passed the European Communities Act and in 1973 Britain joined the Community. The organisation had been established sixteen years earlier with the Treaty of Rome when the six original members – Belgium, France, Holland, Italy, Luxembourg and West Germany – agreed to form the *'Common Market'*. The 1973 enlargement, when Denmark and Eire along with the U.K. joined the Community, has been followed by further expansion with the entry of Greece, Portugal and Spain.

Any European country can apply to join the Community and the main advantage of membership arises from the size of the overall market. The U.K. is a member of a market of over 350 million which represents a seven-fold increase in the potential market for British goods.

17.8.1 The meaning of an 'economic community'

A notion fundamental to the creation of the Community was the creation of a 'common market' – an organisation of the economies of member countries to allow them to act in unison. The best example of a common policy in action has been in agriculture.

The aims of the Community extend far beyond a common market for goods though, towards harmonisation of its members' economies and this has implications in the following areas:

a) *Taxes.* No appreciable difference between the rates and methods of taxes. VAT is the basic form of indirect tax throughout the Community.
b) *Competition.* Regulation of competition throughout the Community to prevent distortions in trade.
c) *Free movement of labour.* Citizens of member states free to work anywhere within the Community.
d) *Free movement of capital.* No restrictions on capital transfers between countries.
e) *A common regional policy.* Any areas throughout the Community with economic problems to be assisted.
f) *Complete monetary integration.* Through the European Monetary System (EMS) all member states' currencies have fixed exchange rates within narrow limits. Another element of EMS is the eventual development of a common Community currency.

A customs union
The Community is a customs union which involves the abolition of tariffs between member countries and the imposition of a common external tariff (CET) on goods from the rest of the world. This means that imports from external countries receive the same treatment – a necessary safeguard to ensure that imports do not flood into the country with the lowest tariffs.

When the U.K. joined the Community, it was only following the trend of its own trade due to the fact that the European market has occupied a larger share of U.K. trade over recent years. Changes in the pattern of trade since we joined the Community can be seen from the figures in Tables 17.4 and 17.5.

Table 17.4 Value of U.K. exports: Analysis by destination

				(£m)
	1987	1988	1989	1990
European Community	39 415	40 938	47 140	55 071
Rest of Western Europe	7 621	7 411	8 120	8 234
North America	12 992	12 795	14 346	14 973
Total Trade	79 849	81 655	93 249	102 479

Table 17.5 Value of U.K. imports: Analysis by source

	1987	1988	1989	(£m) 1990
European Community	49 555	55 807	63 495	65 955
Rest of Western Europe	12 884	14 029	15 349	17 256
North America	10 781	12 903	15 185	16 751
Total Trade	94 026	106 571	120 788	128 624

(Source: C.S.O.)

Exercises

17.1 a) With respect to the theory of international trade, explain the terms;
   i) absolute advantage
   ii) comparative advantage.
   b) The man-hours required to produce 1 car and 1 unit of corn in the United Kingdom and Italy are given in the following schedule:

	UK	Italy
Cars	30	60
Corn	10	40

Giving reasons, indicate whether either has a comparative advantage in: i) cars ii) corn.

(ISVA)

17.2 The production possibilities in countries X and Y are shown in the following table. Prior to specialisation and trade, the optimum product mix for country X is alternative II, and for country Y it is alternative IV.

Alternative production combinations

	I	II	III	IV	V	VI
Country X Excavators	45	36	27	18	9	0
Cars	0	9	18	27	36	45
Country Y Excavators	15	12	9	6	3	0
Cars	0	6	12	18	24	30

   a) Which country should specialise in the production of each good?
   b) What is the total gain from specialisation?
   c) What are the limits to the terms of trade?
   d) If the countries agree to trade 4 cars for 6 excavators what are the gains for each country?
17.3 Discuss the arguments for and against international free trade.
17.4 Examine the effects on the U.K. balance of payments of each of the following:
   a) A British company purchases timber from Russia, and Russian ships are used to transport the cargo to the U.K.
   b) A British quantity surveyor obtains a contract to work in Nigeria and periodically sends money home to his family in the U.K.
   c) A consortium of Arab oil sheikhs purchases a chain of British hotels.
17.5 What measures can a government take to attempt to increase its country's exports? What disadvantages may arise from these courses of action?

Answers to Exercises

Notes to Answers Section

The purpose of this manual is to enable students to use the textbook as effectively as possible by providing 'suggested' answers to the exercises accompanying each chapter.

For many of the shorter, calculation-type questions, full answers are provided, but for the longer essay-type questions, provision of a model answer would be impossible. In the latter case, notes are restricted to the main points which could be used to form the basis of an answer.

In some cases, no specific answer is provided for an exercise. Such a situation occurs whenever it is felt that the question is answered directly in the text, or that the answers to other exercises in that section cover similar ground.

Finally, it must be stressed that the answers given to the questions taken from professional examination papers represent merely the author's own personal interpretation and are in no way 'official' specimen answers.

Chapter One

1.1 a) False. Even in a country which may be described as 'rich', economic resources are still scarce or limited and we are still faced with the necessity of making choices at both an individual and government levels.

Without a doubt, our economy possesses large amounts of some resources but even these are not infinitely large supplies.

b) True. There are only so many workers in the labour force, only so much land on which to build and to grow crops, only a certain number of machines and factories. If all these resources are fully employed, then the production of extra units of product X must entail the sacrifice of some amount of product Y.

c) False. Unless it is specified that the statement refers purely to resources that are limited in supply. In which case there is an opportunity cost in terms of an alternative which has to be given up.

1.3 a)

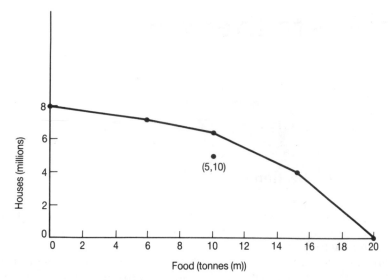

If 10 million tonnes of food are produced, then the rest of the resources in this economy have the capacity to produce an output of 6 million houses. Some resources are therefore being under- or unutilised and the society is not on its production possibility curve as shown in the diagram.

Generally, there must be mismanagement in the economy to put it into this state of unemployment, as the economic system used to allocate resources must be inefficient.

b)

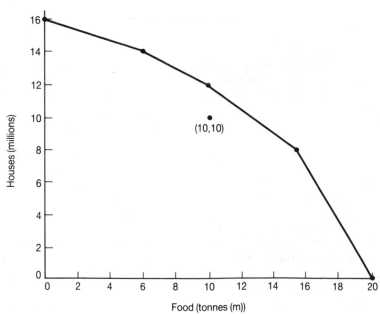

As before, spare capacity still exists and the criticism of inefficiency still holds.

Chapter Two

2.3 There are several possible reasons why consumer sovereignty might not exist in our economy:
   a) There may be insufficient information available to the consumer concerning the characteristics and qualities of products on offer in the market.
   b) There may be a great deal of misrepresentation on the part of producers making it difficult for consumers to find out about the true qualities of products.
   c) There may be insufficient competition among firms in the economy to provide the desired assortment of goods.

It is worthwhile here, to distinguish between consumer sovereignty and consumer choice. Consumer sovereignty relates to the output mix in the economy being determined by the power of consumers' money, but consumer choice relates to the freedom to choose among the goods that can be produced in the economy. It is possible to have a situation where consumer sovereignty exists but little consumer choice does. An example in point being restrictions by the authorities, via planning and building regulations, on the types of houses that consumers are able to have built.

Chapter Three

3.1 In any cost-benefit analysis, decisions have to be made concerning whose costs and benefits would be relevant.

In this example it is obviously necessary to go much wider than just those covered by the commercial accounts of the airport authority, as the project has consequences for the region as a whole.

The main elements to be considered in this type of study are likely to be:
   i) Land and construction costs. The capital costs of planning, designing and constructing the runways, terminal buildings and associated facilities. The compulsory purchase of land close to the airport may not reflect its full market value.
   ii) Road and rail transport costs and benefits. Capital outlay required to improve communication links with the airport. Travel time savings for existing and new airport users; also indirect costs (congestion) and benefits for other users of the transport system.
   iii) Noise and environmental costs. Aircraft noise imposes costs on the community (though the people in the area are already accustomed to this nuisance and may be somewhat physically insensitive to the additional nuisance).
   iv) Costs of a change in land-use resulting from the expansion. The loss of agricultural or industrial output.
   v) Air traffic. Costs of having to relocate airlines; operational restrictions due to proximity to the city.

vi) Labour. Direct employment opportunities arise from the construction work and staff expansion at the airport.

vii) Wider economic and planning considerations. Improved regional air services have an effect on the economic development of the region. Improvements in the means of physical communication should promote faster regional growth. New opportunities for the region to sell to markets not previously accessible may induce the location of new industrial plants in the area.

3.2 On the basis of the information given it is possible to put forward a case for any one of three programmes to be undertaken.

i)   The authority undertaking the development may choose the programme which shows the largest overall net benefit – programme B.

ii) Instead, the investment yielding the best 'value for money' in terms of benefit per £ spent might be chosen – programme A.

iii) Alternatively, the authorities may wish to launch as big a development programme as possible as long as there is at least a net benefit from the investment. So programme D could be justified.

   As the authorities must have at least £36m available in order to be able to consider alternative D, the final choice must depend upon the alternative uses to which the funds not used for the programme might be put.

3.3 The net benefit from the two alternative projects can be considered. This shows that the extra money spent on the building of the road from Y to Z could not be justified.

   The initial outlay of £100m to take the road from X to Y produces a net benefit of £40m and it is therefore a viable project. But the marginal net benefit from the additional outlay of £40m is negative as the extra benefit produced is only £30m.

   The road should end at Y.

Chapter Four

4.1

Quantity demanded (000s)	Price (£)	Quantity supplied (000s)	Surplus (+) or shortage (−)
110	120	91	−19
105	130	92	−13
100	140	94	− 6
95	150	95	0
90	160	97	+ 7
80	170	99	+19
75	180	100	+25

a) The equilibrium price is therefore £150, at which price 95 000 frames are bought and sold.

b) At a price of £170 the producers would be left with a surplus of 19 000 window frames per period. In this situation, a rational producer would be expected to both lower his selling price and reduce the number of frames on the market until the equilibrium price and quantity were restored.

c) The cross-price demand schedule indicates a positive relationship between the price of metal window frames and the demand for wooden frames. This is an obvious indication that the two products are substitutes. In fact, a comparison between the two demand schedules shows them to be very close substitutes.

4.2 In each example, there is assumed to be an initial equilibrium price level of OP at which Oq houses are bought and sold.

After the change in conditions, the price level changes to OP_1 with Oq_1 as the appropriate level of activity.

a)

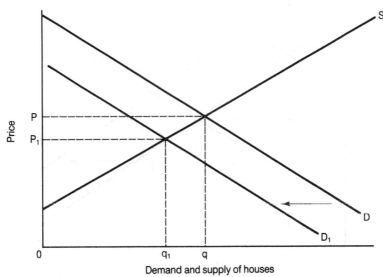

Demand and supply of houses

The rise in interest rates may put the possibility of house purchase beyond the means of some would-be buyers and reduce the effective demand.

The leftward shift of the demand curve produces a lowering of the price level and lessens activity in the market.

b)

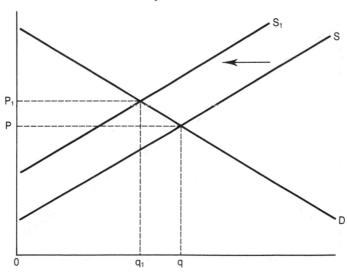

The wage rise constitutes an increase in production costs for the housebuilder and his attempts to pass on the cost to the purchaser produces a leftward shift in the supply curve of (new) houses, and a movement along the demand curve to a higher equilibrium price level. (It may be more logical to assume that the curve becomes more elastic but it should be noted at this point that attempts to distinguish between the availability of houses in general and the supply of new houses are not really being made in this simplified analysis.)

c)

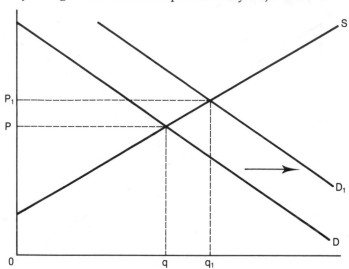

Renting a council house and the purchase of a property for occupation are alternative options for some households.

The reduced availability of such rented accommodation may now force some would-be tenants to consider house purchase and thus the demand for owner-occupied property will shift to the right. This will cause an increase in prices.

d)

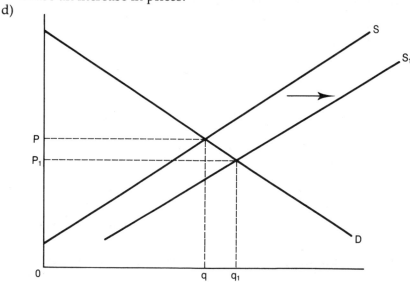

As the cost of the land constitutes a significant proportion of the cost of a new house, this change in supply conditions should produce a reduction in the price of (new) housing and also provide a stimulus to house builders.

4.3 Again the starting point for the analysis is taken to be a situation of 'normal' supply and demand curves.

i)

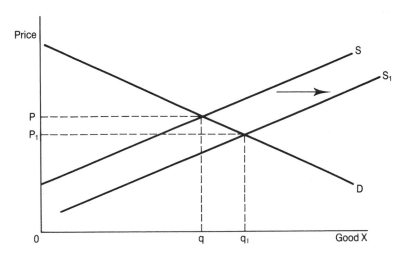

On the assumption that the technical improvement makes it possible to produce good X more cheaply, then at any given price, a producer should now be willing to make available some units of the good which it was previously unprofitable to produce.

The supply curve therefore shifts to the right thereby causing the price to fall and the quantity sold to rise.

ii)

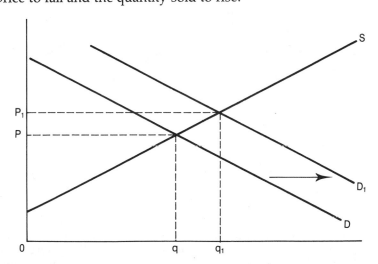

If good X is a normal good then, as consumers' incomes increase, it can be expected that each consumer is likely to purchase more units of X at any given price.

This means a rightward shift in the demand curve and a consequential rise in price and quantity sold.

iii)

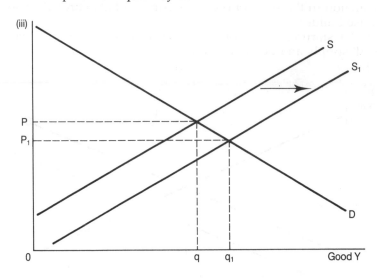

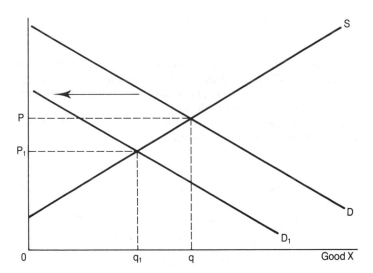

With a fall in the production costs of Y, the supply curve shifts to the right bringing about a reduction in the price of the good.

As Y is now relatively cheaper, the demand conditions for good X are changed and the demand curve for X shifts to the left resulting in a fall in price for X.

Note that there is a fall in the price of both goods X and Y. However, the price fall of the former arises from a leftward shift of the demand curve and means that the quantity demanded falls, whereas for good Y a movement down the demand curve causes the quantity demanded to rise.

4.5 This statement should not of course be taken at face value. An answer to this question should involve an explanation of the difference between a change in the quantity demanded caused by: (i) a movement along a demand curve and (ii) a shift in a demand curve.

The good in question could be one for which there is an abnormal upward sloping demand curve, (see diagram (i)), but the more probable explanation for the situation observed is that a change in demand conditions has produced a rightward shift of the demand curve. This movement along the supply curve in diagram (ii) means that there is a rise in the amount bought at a higher price.

(i)

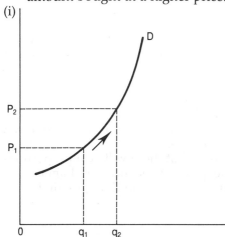

(ii)

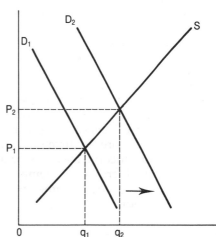

4.6 a) Price elasticity of demand $= \dfrac{\dfrac{70-80}{70}}{\dfrac{160-140}{160}} = \dfrac{-\frac{1}{7}}{\frac{1}{8}} = (-)1.14$

b) Price elasticity of demand $= \dfrac{\dfrac{70-40}{70}}{\dfrac{160-200}{160}} = \dfrac{-\frac{3}{7}}{\frac{1}{4}} = (-)1.71$

4.7 Although an example on the calculation of elasticity of supply is not shown in the text, it is hoped that the student is able to deduce the formula for elasticity of supply, and be able to apply it.

$$\text{Elasticity of supply} = \frac{\text{Proportionate change in quantity supplied}}{\text{Proportionate change in price}}$$

$$= \frac{\text{Change in quantity supplied}}{\text{Original quantity supplied}} \div \frac{\text{Change in price}}{\text{Original price}}$$

a) $\dfrac{225-280}{280} \div \dfrac{9-10}{10} = 1.96$

b) $\dfrac{170-110}{110} \div \dfrac{8-6}{6} = 1.64$

4.8 The importance of having somewhere to live means that housing must be considered to be a very essential good. In this sense people are forced to accept increases in housing costs in order to acquire this necessity. The price elasticity of demand is, of course, not perfectly inelastic, as increased housing costs may result in deferred marriages etc, and produce a lower demand.

    If the overall housing market is split into the sub-markets of owner-occupation, privately rented and council housing then the fact that a certain degree of substitution may occur, raises the price elasticity in any one sector.

    The main factor affecting the degree of income elasticity is the fact that as people become richer, they generally wish to spend a higher proportion of their income on bigger and better houses. The demand can therefore be said to be income elastic.

4.9 b) i) As demand for the good is price elastic, the firm producing the good has an incentive to lower its price. The reduction in price will induce a proportionately greater increase in the number of units sold and therefore the firm's revenue will increase.

    ii) The income elasticity of unity shows that there will be a proportionate increase in demand for the product as income changes, i.e. continuing income growth will lead to a similar growth in the product's market.

Chapter Five

5.1

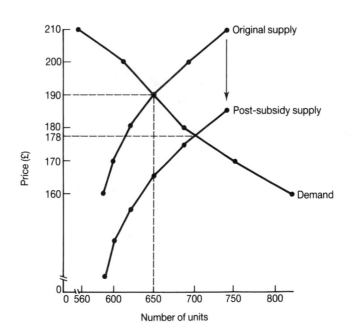

The equilibrium price falls from £190 to £178 as a result of the subsidy.

5.2

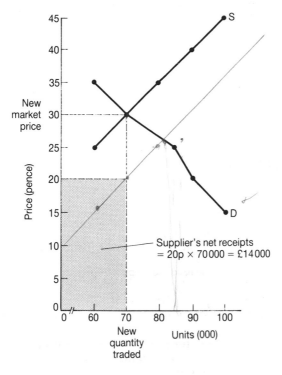

New market supply schedule

Price (pence per unit)	25	30	35	40	45
Quantity supplied (000 units)	60	70	80	90	100

5.3 b) The initial effect of the £5 tax is to produce a £5 increase in the supply schedule prices, as the producer tries to pass on the tax increase in full.

The amended supply schedule (for prices up to £10) is shown together with the original demand schedule.

Price (£)	2	3	4	5	6	7	8	9	10
Quantity demanded (units)	88	82	76	70	64	58	52	46	40
Quantity supplied (units)	–	–	–	–	–	48	52	56	60

i) and ii) The market price and quantity traded are now £8 and 52 units respectively i.e. a price rise for the customer of £2 compared to the pre-tax figure.

iii) The total tax revenue is £(5 × 52) = £260.

5.4

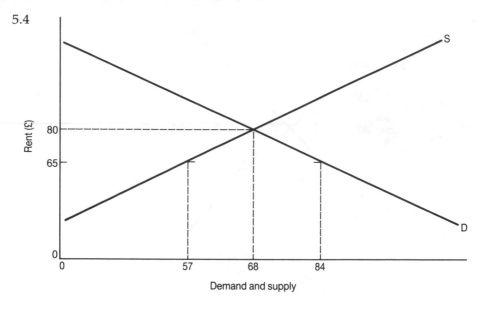

Demand and supply

In a freely operating market situation, the equilibrium rent level would be £80.

At a restricted level of £65 the supply of accommodation is not high enough to meet demand, and excess demand exists in the market. There are therefore 11 households (i.e. the difference between the 68 who would have paid £80 in the free market and the 57 who are able to find accommodation at the restricted rent level) who cannot find accommodation. These households must look towards other sectors of the housing market, such as local authority housing, for accommodation.

5.5 (See answer to previous question for an explanation of the effects of a price restricted to a below free market level).

If the maximum price of a good is set above the free market level, this has no significant effect on the market unless there is a change in the underlying conditions of demand or supply.

The actions of the government in initially imposing the measure may be in anticipation of changing conditions and could in fact even alter producers' profit expectations.

5.6

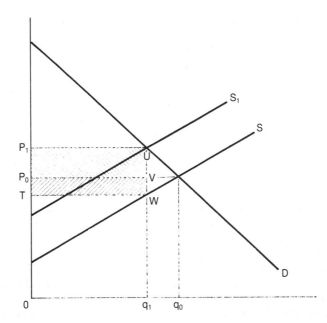

(The tax imposed is assumed to be a specific tax of TP_1 per unit)

The original supply and demand curves give a (pre-tax) price of OP_0 but when the producer tries to pass on the tax in full and the relevant supply curve becomes S_1, the price (to the consumer) rises to OP_1 (Answer (d)).
   The producer only receives (after tax), though, OT per unit (Answer (e)).
   The total tax revenue is TP_1UW (Answer (c)).
   The portion of this tax burden which is met by the consumer is P_0P_1UV (Answer (a)) and the rest (TP_0VW) is met by the producer (Answer (b)).

Chapter Six

6.1

Number of houses	Total cost (£000)	Average cost (£000)	Marginal cost (£000)
0	0	0	
1	64	64	64
2	124	62	60
3	174	58	50
4	228	57	54
5	290	58	62
6	360	60	70

There may be several reasons for the initial reductions in marginal cost, notably: The cost reductions that result from the bulk purchase of materials; plant which was previously underutilised may be used to full capacity at little extra cost; greater co-operation between different types of operative produces fewer delays in the building process.
   Explanations for the subsequent rise in marginal costs include: the need for more plant and operatives to carry out the additional building; having built on the better parts of the site, the builder may find that the costs of

building on the fringe areas are higher, if access is more difficult or if the land presents him with more problems, e.g. the land slopes or more money has to be spent on foundations etc.

6.2   a) 10 pence (£100 per 1000 tiles).

     b) The £200 incurred even if no output is produced.

     c) Profits are maximised at £300 when an output of 8000 tiles is produced. On a marginal basis, the eighth batch of tiles is worth producing because the MC (£80) is less than the MR (£100), but for the ninth batch MC rises to £140 thus exceeding the constant MR and making the batch an uneconomical proposition.

     d) Output (000)

Output (000)	1	2	3	4	5	6	7	8	9
Average cost (£)	280	150	110.3	90	74	63.3	60	62.5	71.1

       Unit cost is at its lowest level of £60 when 7000 tiles are produced.

6.3   To maximise profits he will aim to supply floor space as long as the marginal value is at least as great as the marginal cost involved.

Number of floors	1	2	3	4	5
Marginal Cost (£000)	40	40	40	40	40
Marginal Value (£000)	–	56	52	40	24

The fourth floor is worth building (as long as normal profits are included in the costs).

6.4   In the long-run the builder (as a producer) has to cover all his costs, including his £40 000 fixed costs, but in the short-run he will continue to produce if variable costs are covered. At least some contribution is made towards the fixed costs.

     a) At an output of 3 houses, his losses are minimised and he is at least covering his variable costs.

     b) In this case, he is unable to meet even his variable costs and should not bother to build at all.

6.5 a)

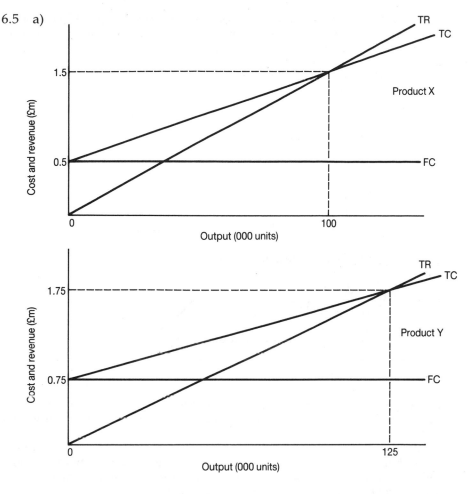

b) As product X has a lower break-even output than product Y, X is more
    profitable up to outputs of 250 000 units, at which output level both
    products are equally profitable.
    i.e. Profit on X = £(150 000 × 5) = £750 000
        Profit on Y = £(125 000 × 6) = £750 000
    If the level of demand rises above 250 000 units, then the profit on
    each extra unit of Y is £1 more than that on each unit of X, and so
    production of Y is more profitable.

6.6 a) In order to calculate the break-even output, the variable cost per unit
    needs to be found.

$$\text{Variable cost per unit} = \frac{11\,000\,000}{45\,000} = £244.44$$

Break-even output =

$$\frac{\text{Fixed costs}}{\text{Price per unit} - \text{Variable cost per unit}} = \frac{6\,000\,000}{400 - 244.44} = 38\,571 \text{ units}$$

Total revenue and costs for this output are £15 428 572.

b) His present profit is £1 000 000, so his new profit target is £1 400 000.

    i)   To raise this extra £400 000 by increasing his unit selling price, this price must rise from £400 to

$$£\left(400 + \frac{400\,000}{45\,000}\right) = £408.88$$

The effect is to lower his break-even volume to:

$$\frac{6\,000\,000}{408.88 - 244.44} = 36\,487 \text{ units}$$

    ii)   If his fixed costs are cut by £400 000 to £5 600 000, his break-even volume falls to:

$$\frac{5\,600\,000}{400 - 144.44} = 36\,000 \text{ units}$$

    iii)   A cut in his variable costs of £400 000 would lower his unit variable cost to:

$$\frac{10\,600\,000}{45\,000} = £235.56$$

The break-even volume then becomes:

$$\frac{6\,000\,000}{400 - 235.56} = 36\,483 \text{ units}$$

6.7   The market supplied by small jobbing builders is a highly competitive one – perhaps one of the closest, in practice, to meet the stringent conditions of perfect competition.

    Any producer who, in a perfectly competitive market, is unable to make a profit must, as a secondary objective, aim to minimise his loss. (His ability to carry such a loss is unlikely to last for long, and if prices do not rise he will be quickly forced out of business.)

    The builder referred to in the diagram finds that if current rates for jobs fall to a level such as Op then he is unable to cover all his costs. This loss is minimised though when he produces an output of Oq, at which marginal cost just equals marginal revenue. A reduction or a rise in this level of output would only lead to an increase in the loss.

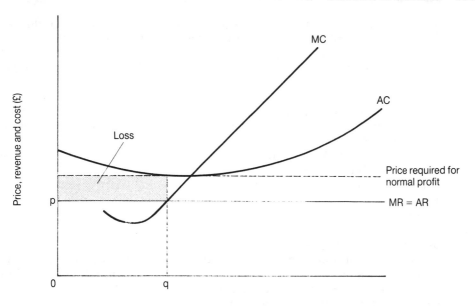

6.8

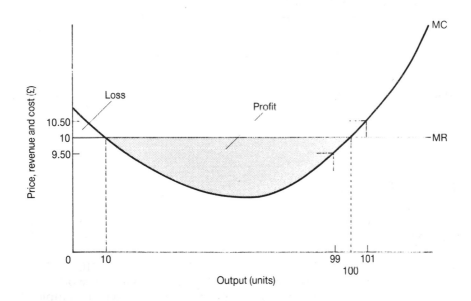

The statement can easily be explained by reference to a diagram showing the short-run situation facing a firm under conditions of perfect competition.

The firm maximises its profits by producing 100 units at a price of £10 each. The 99th unit is just worth producing because the total costs increase by £9.50 when it is produced and so the firm is able to add 50 pence to its supernormal profit. The 100th unit is viable as the extra £10 in revenue just covers costs, but the firm does not find it worthwhile to produce the 101st unit which adds £10.50 to total costs and thereby reduces total supernormal profit by 50 pence.

The firm is making a supernormal profit on all but the first 10 units it produces and this is shown by the fact that the MR line lies above the MC curve between the 10th and 100th units.

On the first 9 units the firm is making a loss. The initial costs of production may be fairly high and the marginal cost of each unit is not covered by the extra revenue received. It is only with the 10th unit that the firm begins to break even.

In this example MC = MR at output levels of 10 and 100 units yet it is the latter which is the profit maximising output. The statement in the question therefore needs qualifying as it is only correct when MC is rising. If MC is falling the point at which it equals MR indicates a loss making output.

6.9 a) True. See Fig. 6.9.
   b) True. Under the normal condition where MR lies below AR.
   c) False. A monopolist may be able to achieve cost savings due to scale economies not available to a small competitive firm, which allow him to charge a lower price and still retain a profit.
   d) True. Under perfect competition.

6.10 a) At all levels of sales, average revenue = £2
      e.g. £40 000/20 000 = £2.
   b) At all levels of sales, marginal revenue = £2
      e.g. For a sales increase from 20 000 to 35 000 units,

$$\text{marginal revenue per unit} = \frac{£70\,000 - 40\,000}{35\,000 - 20\,000}$$

= £30 000/15 000 = £2.

Perfect competition is indicated by this constancy of Price = Average revenue = Marginal revenue.

Chapter Seven

7.1
Numbers of workers	1	2	3	4	5
Marginal physical product	5	7	9	7	4
Marginal revenue product (£)	150	210	270	210	120
Marginal wage cost (£)	210	210	210	210	210

MWC = MRP when 2 workers are employed and when 4 workers are employed, but the firm only begins to 'profit' after 2 workers are employed and so the firm will employ 4.

7.2
Numbers of workers	1	2	3	4	5	6	7
Total physical product (000)	2	5	9	12	14	15	15
Marginal physical product (000)	2	3	4	3	2	1	0
Average physical product (000)	2	2.5	3	3	2.8	2.5	2.1

   a) The most efficient output would normally be determined as that of minimum average cost, but in this example it must be defined in physical terms. The point at which average physical product is highest, when 3 or 4 workers are employed, can be used.

b) MPP is shown in the table. It rises up to the point at which 3 workers are employed and then declines steadily, i.e. diminishing returns set in as it is attempted to raise output by increasing the use of a variable factor (labour) with other factors fixed.

7.5 a) and c) Once in private practice, he still presumably has the option of returning to work as a government valuer. In which case, £1200 is the value of his transfer earnings and also the reward forgone, i.e. his opportunity cost.

b) His economic rent is the difference between his earnings in private practice and this opportunity cost of £1200, i.e. £300.

d) His quasi-economic rent earnings cannot be determined from the data presented.

The extent to which his economic rent will persist, depends upon the existence of the public/private sector differential. This is determined by such factors as growth in demand for valuers in the two sectors and perhaps (in the public sector) by the ability of organised labour to negotiate wage increases.

7.6 a) On the basis that only B is interested in leasing the plot of land, unless C accepts B's offer, his return from the land must be £0, i.e. a zero opportunity cost. In other words, the £200 he receives must be totally economic rent.

b) Now that there are two potential users of the plot, there must be an 'opportunity forgone'. The opportunity cost is now the sum that could be obtained from B (i.e. £200) and so the economic rent of the plot is £(800 − 200) = £600.

7.7 a) True. Given a normal demand for the product.

b) False. It moves in the opposite direction.

c) False. The MRP curve will not be affected. (The marginal cost of the factor will rise though.)

Chapter Eight

8.2 A discussion of the use of industrialised building systems is pertinent here.

For an industry to be able to apply methods of production which yield maximum economies of scale, the production process has to be split down into a number of simple, separate operations. Specialist machines and labour methods must be employed on a continuous basis.

This type of process is feasible in the construction industry with system building, where factory-produced, prefabricated components – ceiling and floor panels, wall sections etc – are erected on site. This allows the transfer of the building process from the site, where the working environment may be poor, to the factory where conditions and quality control are better.

Mass production of components, compared to traditional building methods may provide significant economies of scale in the production of buildings.

Such building methods, however are only really feasible for sustained programmes of building, such as large public housing estates in new town developments. Where demand is intermittent, as is usually the case with most types of building, industrialised building methods are liable to be

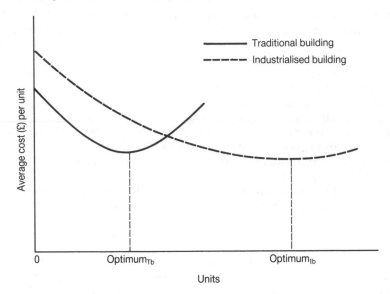

uneconomical as they tend to incorporate more expensive materials and a large capital outlay is required to produce components.

Chapter Twelve

12.1 For people who borrow money to finance the purchase of a house, interest payments may be deducted from income before being assessed for tax. This means that house buyers are being subsidised. Fewer people would wish to borrow money if the tax relief were removed and the demand for house purchase would fall.

　　The market would respond by lowering prices to reflect the value of the lost tax relief.

　　The main problems would obviously be for the construction industry as much housebuilding would cease to be worthwhile, and also for those people who had just purchased property and would have to sustain capital losses.

Chapter Thirteen

13.1 a) If the returns to each project are spread evenly throughout each year then project X is the better investment. It has a pay-back period of 2.5 years compared to the 2.8 years over which the capital outlay on project B is recouped.

　　b) The ARR on project X = $\dfrac{\dfrac{100\,000}{80\,000} \times 100\%}{4} = 31.25\%$

The ARR on project Y = $\dfrac{\dfrac{120\,000}{85\,000} \times 100\%}{4}$ = 35.29%

The preferred project is project Y.

13.2 Scheme A

Year	Cash flow £	PV factor 10%	PV £
0	−1 000 000	1	−1 000 000
1	100 000	0.9091	90 910
2	100 000	0.8264	82 640
3	100 000	0.7513	75 130
4	1 200 000	0.6830	819 600
		NPV =	£68 280

Scheme B

Year	Cash flow £	PV factor 10%	PV £
0	−1 000 000	1	−1 000 000
1	50 000	0.9091	45 455
2	70 000	0.8264	57 848
3	90 000	0.7513	67 617
4	1 300 000	0.6830	887 900
		NPV =	£58 820

Using a discount rate of 10% the cash flow associated with scheme A shows a higher NPV than that of scheme B; the total returns on scheme B might be higher but the incidence of the higher returns on scheme A in years 1 to 3 more than compensates for this factor.

13.3 a)   Project A

Year	Cash flow £	PV factor 10%	PV £
0	−30 000	1	−30 000
1	5 000	0.9091	4 545.5
2	10 000	0.8264	8 264
3	15 000	0.7513	11 269.5
4	20 000	0.6830	13 660
5	20 000	0.6209	12 418
		NPV =	£20 157

Project B

Year	Cash flow £	PV factor 10%	PV £
0	−32 000	1	−32 000
1	20 000	0.9091	18 182
2	15 000	0.8264	12 396
3	15 000	0.7513	11 269.5
4	10 000	0.6830	6 830
5	5 000	0.6209	3 104.5
		NPV =	£19 782

Under the NPV method, using a 10% discount rate, project A is preferred to B.

b)

Project A

Year	Cash Flow £	PV factor 28%	PV £	PV factor 29%	PV £
0	−30 000	1	−30 000	1	−30 000
1	5 000	0.7813	3 906.5	0.7752	3 876
2	10 000	0.6104	6 104	0.6009	6 009
3	15 000	0.4768	7 152	0.4658	6 987
4	20 000	0.3725	7 450	0.3611	7 222
5	20 000	0.2910	5 820	0.2799	5 598
			NPV = £432.5		NPV = −£308

The IRR on project A lies between 28% and 29%.
By interpolation it can be calculated to be just over 28.5%.

Project B

Year	Cash flow £	PV factor 39%	PV £
0	−32 000	1	−32 000
1	20 000	0.7194	14 388
2	15 000	0.5176	7 764
3	15 000	0.3724	5 586
4	10 000	0.2679	2 679
5	5 000	0.1927	963.5
		NPV =	−£619.5

When discounted at 39% the NPV of the cash flow for project B is negative but the IRR is obviously considerably higher than that for project A. (It works out to be 37.6%.)
Using the IRR method project B is preferred.

c) The reason for these conflicting decisions is the variation in the cash flow patterns. A relatively low discount rate of 10% does not greatly penalise A's high returns in years 4 and 5 whereas a high rate provides a low discount factor for these later years.

More information is required before a decision can be made as to the better project. An important factor is the relative degree of certainty that can be attached to the cash flows. The estimates for the final years of the projects may well be much more uncertain. The choice of discount rate must also be examined. If the going rate of return is 10% then these projects may represent a one-off opportunity for the investor and more emphasis can be given to the NPV appraisal result than if the going rate for future projects can also be expected to be thirty-odd per cent.

13.4 The NPV of the cash flow for each method can be used as the basis for comparison.

Method 1

Year	Cash flow £	PV factor 10%	PV £
0	300 000	1	300 000
1	–	0.9091	–
2	50 000	0.8264	41 320
3	–	0.7513	–
4	50 000	0.6830	34 150
5	–	0.6209	–

PV = £375 470

Method 2

Year	Cash flow £	PV factor 10%	PV £
0	200 000	1	200 000
1	40 000	0.9091	36 364
2	40 000	0.8264	33 056
3	40 000	0.7513	30 052
4	40 000	0.6830	27 320
5	40 000	0.6209	24 836

PV = £351 628

In this case all the cash flow figures are outlays and the builder's concern is to ensure that his costs are kept as low as possible.

He should choose Method 2 because the total outlay required, in present value terms, is considerably lower.

(Even though in aggregate terms the money outlay is £400 000 in both methods, the smaller initial outlay in the second method makes it more favourable.)

Chapter Fourteen

14.1   National Income is measured in three different ways, by finding:
   i)   The value of the output of all the goods and services produced in the economy.
   ii)   The value of all the various types of income that arise.
   iii)   The value of total expenditure in the economy.

   National Output = National Income = National Expenditure
   (If the economy is in equilibrium)

   This can be basically shown by a circular flow diagram in which the flow is cut through at three different points

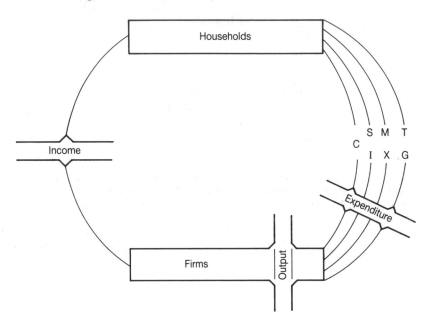

14.2   In this economy the equilibrium level of income must occur where:

$$Y = C + S \text{ and } Y = C + I$$
$$\text{so } S = I$$

If I = £20 000m = S, then Y − C must equal £20 000m.
   From the table it can be seen that this only holds at an income level of £120 000m.

Income (£m)	Consumer expenditure (£m)	Savings (£m)
80 000	70 000	10 000
100 000	85 000	15 000
120 000	100 000	20 000
140 000	115 000	25 000
160 000	130 000	30 000

14.3 The completed table is:

	Period I	Period II
National Income (£m)	50 000	55 000
Consumption (£m)	47 500	52 250
Saving (£m)	2 500	2 750
Investment (£m)	2 500	2 750

The marginal propensity to consume is 0.95 (=47 500/50 000) and so in Period II, 52 250 = 0.95 × National Income, and National Income must be 55 000.

As National Income = Consumption − Saving, in period I
Saving = 50 000 − 47 500 = 2500 and in period II,
Saving = 55 000 − 52 250 = 2750.
In equilibrium Saving = Investment in both periods.
The Multiplier =

$$\frac{1}{1 - \text{marginal propensity to consume}} = \frac{1}{1 - 0.95} = 20$$

14.4 The fall in the level of government spending represents a reduction in the level of 'injection' into the circular flow.

The consequential effects on the level of income are determined by the Multiplier in operation. In this example the Multiplier is:

$$\frac{1}{1 - 0.8} = 5$$

When this is applied to the change in government spending of −£1000m, the level of National Income would be expected to fall by £5000m.

In practice, the consequential effects of the cut should not be so drastic. The expenditure cutback may not be exactly matched by a reduction in taxation but, should the government decide to cut taxes, there may be significant boosts to consumer demand (especially from a cut in income tax) and to investment demand (from a cut in tax on companies' profits).

The cutback in government spending may of course be met from a reduced borrowing requirement. In which case a resultant fall in interest rates should pave the way for higher levels of borrowing and spending by consumers and firms.

14.5 a) The increased taxation represents a leakage from the circular flow. Householders are left with less to spend on consumer goods, and firms are less able to undertake investment. The propensity to consume will fall and so the multiplier effect in operation is reduced.
The likely effect is a reduction in the level of National Income.

b) This means that people must be spending more and so causing the level of aggregate demand to rise. A direct boost to the economy therefore arises from the increased consumer demand and the value of the multiplier also goes up.
National Income will increase.

c) The reduction in the level of this 'injection' causes a fall in aggregate demand. Less demand from abroad has 'multiplied' effects in the economy as the firms that are directly affected may be forced to undertake less investment and employ less workers etc.
National Income will fall.

14.6   a) False. This situation only occurs when the level of aggregate demand is sufficiently high to create full employment.

b) True. There is an increase in the 'leakage' from the circular flow. In itself, a rise in taxation means that people have less money to spend on consumer goods and services if their disposable income falls. Producers are likely to reduce their investment expenditure if their profits are reduced.

(There should of course be positive effects on the level of income if the tax revenue is 'injected' back into the system through increased government expenditure.)

c) True. Increases in consumer spending raise the value of the multiplier and increases in private investment and government spending raise the level of injections to which the multiplier effect can be applied.

One detraction from this effect is that some of this expenditure may be on imported goods causing a 'leakage' from the income flow.

d) False. More saving means that a smaller proportion of income is directly returned to the circular flow. The reduction in consumer spending and the resultant fall in the value of the multiplier will, *per se*, have a depressant effect on the level of income.

14.7   (See previous answer, part (d).) The effects of an increase in saving produce the so-called 'Paradox of Thrift'.

Classical economic theory tended to stress the importance of saving (thrift) for making funds available to allow loans to be made for investment. Yet, in recent times more importance is attached to the direct effects of saving on the level of aggregate demand, and any government wishing to stimulate the economy and raise the level of employment may actively discourage saving.

14.9   a) $TFE = 1+2+3+4+5$

b) $GDP = TFE - 6$

c) $GNP = GDP + 7$

d) $NNP = GNP - 8$

14.10 Using:

Change in income = Change in government expenditure × Multiplier.
The change in income required = −£80 billion.
Therefore −£80 billion = −£20 billion × Multiplier.
Multiplier = 4

As the multiplier $= \dfrac{1}{1-mpc} = 4$

$mpc = 0.75$

Chapter Fifteen

15.1 A major purpose of taxation is to raise revenue. Yet additionally several other objectives are also important in determining the types of taxes levied by the government.

Direct taxes possess certain characteristics, which make them preferable to indirect taxes.

a) A fairer redistribution of income in the economy can be achieved if taxes are based on ability to pay. Income tax lends itself particularly well to being administered on a progressive scale. With a system of personal allowances it also means that poorer households can be exempted from the requirement to pay any income tax.

b) Direct taxes are non-inflationary. Indirect taxes, by their very nature, cause price increases; but direct taxes leave the consumer with less money to spend and reduce the pressure on prices.

c) The revenue obtained by the exchequer from direct taxes can be more easily estimated than that due from indirect taxes where the change in demand for a good resulting from a tax imposition on the price has to be gauged.

The following points may be put forward as some of the more important advantages held by indirect taxes.

For the taxpayer:

a) Greater freedom of choice. A person is left with a greater proportion of his income to spend as he chooses.

b) The taxes are avoidable in the sense that a consumer is free to buy or not to buy a good which bears a tax. Also, the individual can choose when to pay the tax rather than have it decided for him (as is the case with PAYE).

For the government:

c) Expenditure taxes are often 'hidden taxes'. Useful for a government concerned with the disfavour that may result from any rises in the level of taxation. People are always painfully aware of direct deductions from their pay packets, but not mindful of the proportion of the cost of a packet of cigarettes or litre of petrol that goes into the government's coffers.

d) The degree of evasion of payment of indirect taxes is far lower than that of direct taxes and in this sense the tax revenue is more certain.

e) The use of indirect taxes gives the government more power to regulate demand in certain areas of the economy, e.g. a duty on imported vehicles to improve the balance of payments, a tax on fuel to conserve scarce resources etc.

f) Indirect taxes tend not to be as detrimental to production as direct taxes – progressive income taxes reduce the incentive to undertake extra work, profits tax may deter investment.

15.2 a) This should certainly stimulate housebuilding in the private sector. A reduction in costs providing an incentive for speculative housebuilding – some previously non-viable projects now being profitable. If this extra finance for subsidies were additional to that already being spent on the public sector, some of the pressure on the demand for housing in this sector might be relieved.

b) The implementation of such a tax might take the form of perhaps site value rating by local authorities – a tax on the open market value of a site on the basis that it is currently available for its most profitable use.

The tax should improve the efficiency of land use. An incentive is provided to undertake improvements to property, to develop sites to their most profitable use and to deter hoarding.

c) Demand in general in the economy is stimulated. Consumers have more money to spend on goods including housing and, via the acceleration effect, an increased demand for new industrial and commercial building will arise.

15.3 i) Marginal tax rate $= \dfrac{\text{Total tax paid} - \text{Total tax paid before income rise}}{\text{Rise in income}}$

ii) Original average tax rate $= \dfrac{\text{Original total tax paid}}{\text{Original total income}}$

iii) Final average tax rate $= \dfrac{\text{Final total tax paid}}{\text{Final total income}}$

a) i) $\dfrac{7.50}{30} = 25\%$ ii) $\dfrac{30}{150} = 20\%$ iii) $\dfrac{37.50}{180} = 20.8\%$

b) i) $\dfrac{2}{30} = 6.7\%$ ii) $\dfrac{15}{150} = 10\%$ iii) $\dfrac{17}{180} = 9.4\%$

c) i) $\dfrac{37.50}{30} = 125\%$ ii) $\dfrac{30}{150} = 20\%$ iii) $\dfrac{67.50}{180} = 37.5\%$

d) i) $\dfrac{15}{30} = 50\%$ ii) $\dfrac{75}{150} = 50\%$ iii) $\dfrac{90}{180} = 50\%$

A tax on income may be levied on a constant, regressive or progressive scale.

In situation d) the tax is levied at a constant 50% rate. At the different levels of income the average tax rate remains the same. Situation b) depicts a regressive tax. As income increases the proportion paid in tax reduces, because the marginal tax rate is lower than the original average.

The taxes in cases a) and c) are progressive. The marginal rate being higher than the original average rate, therefore produces an increase in the average rate. In a) the tax is mildly progressive but in c) the individual is actually worse off as a result of the rise in income. (An unlikely but not totally inconceivable occurrence.)

Progressiveness is often deemed to be a desirable attribute for a tax to possess and income taxes are particularly suitable to administer on a progressive scale.

Chapter Sixteen

16.1 a) The answer depends upon whether or not the money supply remains fixed or whether it is reduced as income declines.

If it is reduced then it is difficult to maintain precautionary balances at their previous level. If it remains at the same level, then as the transactions demand falls, more money is available for precautionary and speculative purposes and these holdings may increase.

b) The level of demand is likely to fall as less money needs to be held to cover unexpected expenditure when the gap between pay days is reduced.

c) The reduction in concern for having to meet unforeseen expenditure lowers the level of demand.

16.2 a) The going rate of interest in this economy is determined by the level at which:

Total supply of money = Total demand for money
= Demand for asset money + demand for active balances

∴ £24 000m = Demand for asset money + £8000m

∴ Demand for asset money = £16 000m

This level of demand occurs at a rate of interest of 6%.

b) If the total supply of money were reduced by £8000 to £16 000m then the equilibrating demand for asset money must also be reduced by £8000m to a level of £8000m.

This would have the effect of raising the interest rate to 7%.

c) The rise in the rate of interest may deter some firms from borrowing funds for investment.

16.3 a) The money supply falls by £8000m,

i.e. $\dfrac{100}{12.5} \times £1000m$, as the banks' liquidity is reduced.

b) The money supply increases by £16 000m,

i.e. $\dfrac{100}{12.5} \times £2000m$, as liquidity is raised.

c) The credit multiplier rises from 8 to 10 which means that the banks are able to reduce their reserves (and increase the money supply by 25%).

Chapter Seventeen

17.1 a) Adam Smith put forward the proposition that if one of two countries could produce one product more efficiently and more cheaply than the other country, and if the other country could produce a second product more efficiently and cheaply, then there would be obvious gains for them from specialisation and trade. Both would benefit from specialising in the product in which they had an absolute advantage.

Ricardo took this proposition a stage further with the view that it is comparative advantage that is important. One country could be more efficient at producing both products but it could still benefit both countries if the more efficient country specialised in the production of, and exported, the good for which it had the greater comparative advantage. He explained his argument in terms of the labour costs involved in producing the different products, a notion used for the example in part b).

b) The U.K. has an absolute advantage in both cars and corn. It can produce both more efficiently than Italy. However, the U.K. is relatively more efficient at producing corn.

Italy though, has a comparative advantage in cars, which it is able to produce with twice the man hours needed in the U.K., whereas the production of corn requires four times the man hours.

Each country can gain if each specialises in and exports the product for which it has the comparative advantage.

17.2 a) The country with the absolute advantage in both types of production is country X.

If each uses all its resources to produce excavators, country X is able to produce three times as many as is country Y, but in the production of cars the comparable ratio is only one and a half to one.

Country X therefore has a relative advantage in excavators and should specialise in that product whilst country Y specialises in cars.

b) With specialisation, country X is able to produce 45 excavators and country Y produces 30 cars. Compared to the previous optimum product mix for both countries, there is a net gain of $(45 - 36 - 6 =)$ 3 excavators and $(30 - 9 - 18 =)$ 3 cars.

c) By its own efforts country X is able internally to exchange cars for excavators at the rate of $1:1$ (i.e. the opportunity cost of producing one excavator is one car). To persuade country X to trade, the exchange rate of cars for excavators must be greater than $1:1$.

To obtain excavators by switching its own resources, country Y has to give 2 cars for every excavator. The exchange rate with country X must therefore be less than 2 cars: 1 excavator, otherwise country Y will not trade.

d) It is unlikely that country X would agree to such a trade. Country Y would be better-off to the tune of 8 cars. (It would now have 6 excavators and 26 cars, yet could only produce 6 excavators and 18 cars by its own efforts.) Country X, however, with a post-trade position of 39 excavators and 4 cars, is 2 cars worse-off than it would be if, by its own efforts, it produced 39 excavators and used the rest of its resources to produce cars.

17.3 The main arguments in favour of allowing international trade to take place free of interference are:

i)   Consumers in a country are able to obtain a wider variety of goods than that country may be able to produce, and are also able to benefit from higher standards of living.

ii) Higher employment results in those industries able to sell to a larger market area.

iii) Larger outputs due to increased markets can result in economies of scale and lower product prices in home markets.

iv) Advances in technology are spread to other countries.

In spite of these arguments, a case for interference with trade and trade protection can be based on the following:

v)   Import tariffs can be an important source of tax revenue for the government.

vi) Developing countries may feel the need to protect 'infant industries' from foreign competitors who hold a cost advantage or may even want to 'dump' their products.

vii) In developed countries with relatively high-cost labour, workers may desire protection from cheap-labour goods from abroad.

viii) Import tariffs and export subsidies can play important roles in policies of balance of payments correction.

ix) The ultimate reason is that as other countries undertake protective measures, no one country can afford to go it alone.

17.4 a) Both a visible and an invisible import. The current account is adversely affected as payment has to be made for the timber itself and also for its shipment.

b) A private transfer produces a credit item with these payments by the expatriate worker to his dependants in the U.K.

c) A flow of investment funds into the U.K. from overseas. The future effects of this inflow of capital may be outflows of profits etc from the investment, shown as debit items in the invisible sector.

17.5 Of the various alternative measures – such as export subsidies, tax concessions for exporters, anti-inflation policy etc – it is probably the problems associated with the devaluation of the currency which a student should most appreciate.

With an understanding of the concept of elasticity of demand, the possible revenue consequences of a fall in the prices of a country's goods overseas should be considered.

Index